AS

MEI STRUCTURED MATHEMATICS

SECOND EDITION

Sta

Antho

Alan G

Liam H

Roger

Series

Hodder & Stou

A MEMBER OF THE HODDER

Acknowledgements

We are grateful to the following companies, institutions and individuals who have given permission to reproduce photographs in this book. Every effort has been made to trace and acknowledge ownership of copyright. The publishers will be glad to make suitable arrangements with any copyright holders whom it has not been possible to contact.

Photographs supplied by Andrew Lambert (pages 80 and 122), Colin Taylor Productions (pages 112 and 156), Hodder Picture Library (page 2), Life File/ Emma Lee (pages 128 and 142), Life File/Nigel Shuttleworth (page 137)

OCR, AQA and Edexcel accept no responsibility whatsoever for the accuracy or method of working in the answers given.

Orders: please contact Bookpoint Ltd, 78 Milton Park, Abingdon, Oxon OX14 4TD. Telephone: (44) 01235 827720, Fax: (44) 01235 400454. Lines are open from 9.00–6.00, Monday to Saturday, with a 24 hour message answering service. Email address: orders@bookpoint.co.uk

British Library Cataloguing in Publication Data
A catalogue record for this title is available from The British Library

ISBN 0 340 771976
First published 1993
Second edition published 2000
Impression number   10 9 8 7 6 5 4 3 2
Year   2005 2004 2003 2002 2001 2000

Copyright © 1993, 2000 Anthony Eccles, Alan Graham, Terry Heard, Liam Hennessy, Roger Porkess

Typeset by Aarontype Ltd, Easton, Bristol.
Printed in Great Britain for Hodder & Stoughton Educational, a division of Hodder Headline Plc, 338 Euston Road, London NW1 3BH by J. W. Arrowsmith Ltd, Bristol.

MEI Structured Mathematics

Mathematics is not only a beautiful and exciting subject in its own right but also one that underpins many other branches of learning. It is consequently fundamental to the success of a modern economy.

MEI Structured Mathematics is designed to increase substantially the number of people taking the subject post-GCSE, by making it accessible, interesting and relevant to a wide range of students.

It is a credit accumulation scheme based on 45 hour modules which may be taken individually or aggregated to give Advanced Subsidiary (AS) and Advanced GCE (A Level) qualifications in Mathematics, Further Mathematics and related subjects (like Statistics). The modules may also be used to obtain credit towards other types of qualification.

The course is examined by OCR (previously the Oxford and Cambridge Schools Examination Board) with examinations held in January and June each year.

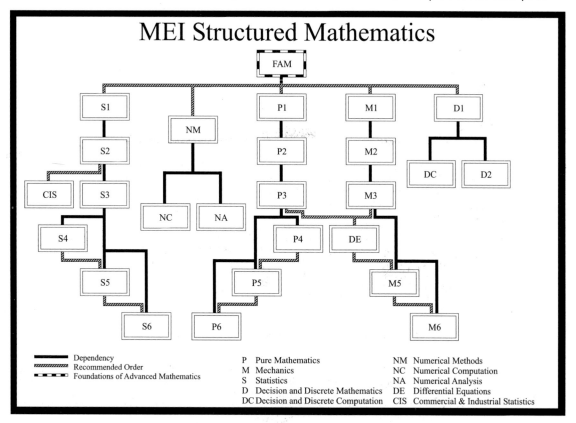

This is one of the series of books written to support the course. Its position within the whole scheme can be seen in the diagram above.

Mathematics in Education and Industry is a curriculum development body which aims to promote the links between Education and Industry in Mathematics at secondary school level, and to produce relevant examination and teaching syllabuses and support material. Since its foundation in the 1960s, MEI has provided syllabuses for GCSE (or O Level), Additional Mathematics and A Level.

For more information about MEI Structured Mathematics or other syllabuses and materials, write to MEI Office, Albion House, Market Place, Westbury, Wiltshire, BA13 3DE.

Introduction

This is the first in a series of books written to support the Statistics modules in MEI Structured Mathematics. They are also suitable for use with other Statistics courses at this level. Throughout, the emphasis is on understanding and interpretation, rather than on mere routine calculations.

This book covers four fundamental aspects of statistics: exploring data, sampling, probability and hypothesis testing.

The first two chapters look at the most appropriate ways of investigating and displaying data sets so that their main features can be communicated. You are encouraged to collect your own figures and get a feel for real data; this involves sampling, the subject of Chapter 4. These topics are supported by coursework in the MEI module; detailed advice on this is available from the MEI office.

The two chapters on probability start with the basic ideas and move on to cover conditional probability and some simple cases involving selections. The book ends with two chapters on the binomial distribution and its use in hypothesis testing. As you go through the subsequent books in the series you will meet and be able to use a steadily increasing number of hypothesis tests.

Several examples are taken from the pages of a fictional local newspaper, the *Avonford Star*. Much of the information which you receive every day comes from the media and is of a broadly statistical nature. In this book you are encouraged to recognise this and to evaluate what you are told.

This is the second edition of this book and some parts of it have been substantially changed. I would like to thank all those who have been involved in this revision work, particularly Liam Hennessy, Charlie Stripp and Terry Heard, and of course the original authors most of whose work is still in place. This edition includes an increased number of past examination questions and I would also like to thank the various examination boards for permission to use them.

Roger Porkess, Series Editor

Contents

1

Exploring data

A judicious man looks at statistics, not to get knowledge but to save himself from having ignorance foisted on him.

Carlyle

The cuttings on page 1 all appeared in one newspaper on one day. Some of them give data as figures, others display them as diagrams.

How do you interpret this information? Which data do you take seriously and which do you dismiss as being insignificant or even misleading?

To answer these questions fully you need to understand how data are collected and analysed before they are presented to you, and how you should evaluate what you are given to read (or see on the television). This is an important part of the subject of statistics.

In this book, many of the examples are set as stories within a fictitious local newspaper, the *Avonford Star*. Some of them are written as articles; others are presented from the journalists' viewpoint as they sort through data trying to write an interesting story. As you work through the book, look too at the ways you are given such information in your everyday life.

THE AVONFORD STAR

Another cyclist seriously hurt.
Will you be next?

On her way back home from school on Wednesday afternoon, little Denise Cropper was knocked off her bicycle and taken to hospital with suspected concussion.

Denise was struck by a Ford Transit van, only 50 metres from her own house.

Denise is the fourth child from the Springfields estate to be involved in a serious cycling accident this year.

The busy road where Denise Cropper was knocked off her bicycle yesterday

---

After this report the editor of the *Avonford Star* commissioned one of the paper's reporters to investigate the situation and write a leading article for the paper on it. She explained to the reporter that there was growing concern locally about cycling accidents involving children. She emphasised the need to collect good quality data to support presentations to the *Star*'s readers.

 Is the aim of the investigation clear?
Is the investigation worth carrying out?
What makes good quality data?

The reporter started by collecting data from two sources. He went through back numbers of the *Avonford Star* for the previous two years, finding all the reports of cycling accidents. He also asked an assistant to carry out a survey of the ages of local cyclists; he wanted to know whether most cyclists were children, young adults or whatever.

? Are the reporter's data sources appropriate?

Before starting to write his article, the reporter needed to make sense of the data for himself. He then had to decide how he was going to present the information to his readers. These are the sorts of data he had to work with.

Name	Age	Distance from home	Cause	Injuries	Treatment
John Smith	45	3 km	skid	Concussion	Hosp. Outpatient
Debbie Lane	5	75 km	hit kerb	Broken arm	Hosp. Outpatient
Arvinder Sethi	12	1200 m	lorry	Multiple fractures	Hosp. 3 weeks
Marion Wren	8	300 m	hit each other	Bruising	Hosp. Outpatient
David Huker	8	50 m	hit each other	Concussion	Hosp. overnight

There were 92 accidents listed in the reporter's table.

Ages of cyclists (from survey)

66	6	62	19	20		15	21	8	21	63		44	10	44	34	18
35	26	61	13	61		28	21	7	10	52		13	52	20	17	26
64	11	39	22	9		13	9	17	64	32		8	9	31	19	22
37	18	138	16	67		45	10	55	14	66		67	14	62	28	36
9	23	12	9	37		7	36	9	88	46		12	59	61	22	49
18	20	11	25	7		42	29	6	60	60		16	50	16	34	14
18	15													

This information is described as *raw data*, which means that no attempt has yet been made to organise it in order to look for any patterns.

Looking at the data

At the moment the arrangement of the ages of the 92 cyclists tells you very little at all. Clearly these data must be organised so as to reveal the underlying shape, the *distribution*. The figures need to be ranked according to size and preferably grouped as well. The reporter had asked an assistant to collect the information and this was the order in which she presented it.

Tally

Tallying is a quick, straightforward way of grouping data into suitable intervals. You have probably met it already.

Stated age (years)	Tally	Frequency
0–9	ЖЖ ЖЖ ЖЖ |||	13
10–19	ЖЖ ЖЖ ЖЖ ЖЖ ЖЖ		26
20–29	ЖЖ ЖЖ ЖЖ		16
30–39	ЖЖ ЖЖ	10
40–49	ЖЖ		6
50–59	ЖЖ	5
60–69	ЖЖ ЖЖ ||||	14
70–79		0
80–89			1
⋮		
130–139			1
	TOTAL	92

Extreme values

A tally immediately shows up any extreme values, that is values which are far away from the rest. In this case there are two extreme values, usually referred to as *outliers*: 88 and 138. Before doing anything else you must investigate these.

In this case the 88 is genuine, the age of Millie Smith, who is a familiar sight cycling to the shops.

The 138 needless to say is not genuine. It was the written response of a man who was insulted at being asked his age. Since no other information about him is available, this figure is best ignored and the sample size reduced from 92 to 91. You should always try to understand an outlier before deciding to ignore it; it may be giving you important information.

 Practical statisticians are frequently faced with the problem of *outlying observations*, observations that depart in some way from the general pattern of a data set. What they, and you, have to decide is whether any such observations belong to the data set or not. In the above example the data value 88 is a genuine member of the data set and is retained. The data value 138 is not a member of the data set and is therefore rejected.

Describing the shape of a distribution

An obvious benefit of using a tally is that it shows the overall shape of the distribution.

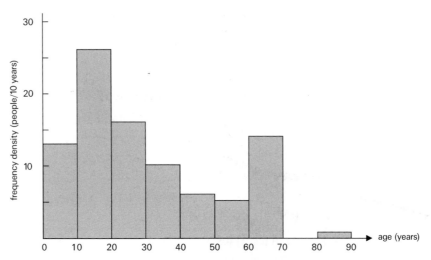

Figure 1.1 *Histogram to show the ages of people involved in cycling accidents*

You can now see that a large proportion (more than a quarter) of the sample are in the 10 to 19 year age range. This is the *modal* group as it is the one with the most members. The single value with the most members is called the *mode*, in this case age 9.

You will also see that there is a second peak among those in their sixties; so this distribution is called *bimodal*, even though the frequency in the interval 20–29 is greater than the frequency in the interval 60–69.

Different types of distribution are described in terms of the position of their modes or modal groups, see figure 1.2.

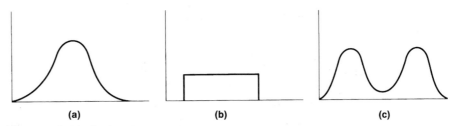

Figure 1.2 *Distribution shapes:*
(a) *unimodal and symmetrical* **(b)** *uniform (no mode but symmetrical)* **(c)** *bimodal*

When the mode is off to one side the distribution is said to be *skewed*. If the mode is to the left with a long tail to the right the distribution has positive or right skewness; if the long tail is to the left the distribution has negative or left skewness. These two cases are shown in figure 1.3.

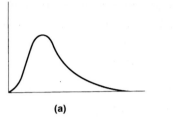 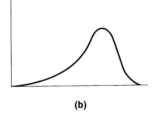

Figure 1.3 *Skewness:* **(a)** *positive* **(b)** *negative*

Stem and leaf diagrams or stemplots

The quick and easy view of the distribution from the tally has been achieved at the cost of losing information. You can no longer see the original figures which went into the various groups and so cannot, for example, tell from looking at the tally whether Millie Smith is 80, 81, 82, or any age up to 89. This problem of the loss of information can be solved by using a *stem and leaf diagram* (or *stemplot*).

This is a quick way of grouping the data so that you can see their distribution and still have access to the original figures. The one below shows the ages of the 91 cyclists surveyed.

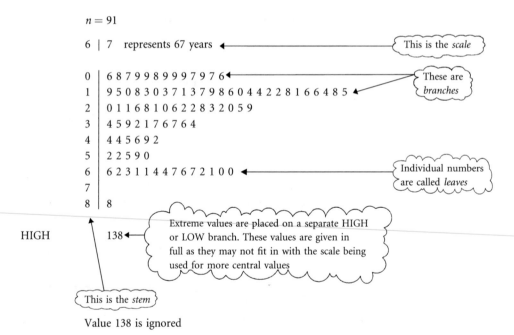

Value 138 is ignored

Figure 1.4 *Stem and leaf diagram showing the ages of a sample of 91 cyclists (unsorted)*

❓ Do all the branches have leaves?

The column of figures on the left (going from 0 to 8) corresponds to the tens digits of the ages. This is called the *stem* and in this example it consists of 9 branches. On each branch on the stem are the *leaves* and these represent the units digits of the data values.

As you can see above, the leaves for a particular branch have been placed in the order in which the numbers appeared in the original raw data. This is fine for showing the general shape of the distribution, but it is usually worthwhile sorting the leaves, as shown in figure 1.5.

$n = 91$

6 | 7   represents 67 years

```
0 | 6 6 7 7 7 8 8 9 9 9 9 9 9
1 | 0 0 0 1 1 2 2 3 3 3 4 4 4 5 5 6 6 6 7 7 8 8 8 8 9 9
2 | 0 0 0 1 1 1 2 2 2 3 5 6 6 8 8 9
3 | 1 2 4 4 5 6 6 7 7 9
4 | 2 4 4 5 6 9
5 | 0 2 2 5 9
6 | 0 0 1 1 1 2 2 3 4 4 6 6 7 7
7 |
8 | 8
```

Note that the value 138 is left out as it has been identified as not belonging to this set of data.

Figure 1.5 *Stem and leaf diagram showing the ages of a sample of 91 cyclists (sorted)*

The stem and leaf diagram gives you a lot of information at a glance:

- The youngest cyclist is 6 and the oldest is 88 years of age
- More people are in the 10–19 year age range than in any other 10 year age range
- There are three 61 year olds
- The modal age (i.e. the age with the most people) is 9
- The 17th oldest cyclist in the survey is 55 years of age.

If the values on the basic stem and leaf diagram are too cramped, that is, if there are so many leaves on a line that the diagram is not clear, you may *stretch* it. To do this you put values 0, 1, 2, 3, 4 on one line and 5, 6, 7, 8, 9 on another. Doing this to the example results in the diagram shown in figure 1.6.

When stretched, this stem and leaf diagram reveals the skewed nature of the distribution.

$n = 91$

6 | 7   represents 67

```
0  |
0  | 6 6 7 7 7 8 8 9 9 9 9 9 9
1* | 0 0 0 1 1 2 2 3 3 3 4 4 4
1  | 5 5 6 6 6 7 7 8 8 8 8 9 9
2* | 0 0 0 1 1 1 2 2 2 3
2  | 5 6 6 8 8 9
3* | 1 2 4 4
3  | 5 6 6 7 7 9
4* | 2 4 4
4  | 5 6 9
5* | 0 2 2
5  | 5 9
6* | 0 0 1 1 1 2 2 3 4 4
6  | 6 6 7 7
7* | ◄─────────────────────
7  |
8* |
8  | 8
```

> You must include all the branches, even those with no leaves

Figure 1.6 *Stem and leaf diagram showing the ages of a sample of 91 cyclists (sorted)*

? How would you squeeze a stem and leaf diagram? What would you do if the data have more significant figures than can be shown on a stem and leaf diagram?

Stem and leaf diagrams are particularly useful for comparing data sets. With two data sets a back-to-back stem and leaf diagram can be used, as shown in figure 1.7.

represents 590   9 | 5 | 2   represents 520

```
        9 | 5 | 1 7
        2 | 6 | 0 2 3 5 8
    5 3 0 | 7 | 1 2 5 6 6 7
9 7 5 1 1 | 8 | 3 5
  8 6 2 1 | 9 | 2
```

> Note that the numbers on the left of the stem still have the smallest number next to the stem

Figure 1.7

? How would you represent positive and negative data on a stem and leaf diagram?

1 Write down the numbers which are represented by this stem and leaf diagram.

$n = 15$

32 | 1   represents 3.21 cm

```
32 | 7
33 | 2 6
34 | 3 5 9
35 | 0 2 6 6 8
36 | 1 1 4
37 | 2
```

2 Write down the numbers which are represented by this stem and leaf diagram.

$n = 19$

8 | 9   represents 0.089 mm

```
 8 | 3 6 7
 9 | 0 1 4 8
10 | 2 3 5 8 9 9
11 | 0 1 4
12 | 3 5
13 | 1
```

3 Show the following numbers on a stem and leaf diagram with six branches, remembering to include the appropriate scale.

0.212   0.223   0.226   0.230   0.233   0.237   0.241   0.242
0.248   0.253   0.253   0.259   0.262

4 Show the following numbers on a stem and leaf diagram with five branches, remembering to include the appropriate scale.

81.07   82.00   78.01   80.08   82.05   81.09   79.04   81.03   79.06   80.04

5 Write down the numbers which are represented by this stem and leaf diagram.

$n = 21$

34 | 5   represents 3.45 m

LOW   0.013, 0.089, 1.79

```
34 | 3
35 | 1 7 9
36 | 0 4 6 8
37 | 1 1 3 8 9
38 | 0 5
39 | 4
```

HIGH   7.42, 10.87

6 Forty motorists entered for a driving competition. The organisers were anxious to know if the contestants had enjoyed the event and also to know their ages, so that they could plan and promote future events effectively. They therefore asked entrants to fill in a form on which they commented on the various tests and gave their ages.

The information was copied from the forms and the ages listed as:

$$
\begin{array}{lllll}
28 & 52 & 44 & 28 & 38 \\
19 & 55 & 34 & 35 & 66 \\
61 & 38 & 26 & 29 & 63 \\
37 & 41 & 39 & 81 & 35 \\
\end{array}
\qquad
\begin{array}{lllll}
46 & 62 & 59 & 37 & 60 \\
37 & 22 & 26 & 45 & 5 \\
38 & 29 & 36 & 45 & 33 \\
35 & 32 & 36 & 39 & 33 \\
\end{array}
$$

(i) Plot these data as an unsorted stem and leaf diagram.

(ii) Identify any outliers and comment on them.

7 The unsorted stem and leaf diagram below gives the ages of males whose marriages were reported in a local newspaper one week.

$n = 42$

1 | 9   represents 19

```
0 |
1 | 9 6 9 8
2 | 5 6 8 9 1 1 0 3 6 8 4 1 2 7
3 | 0 0 5 2 3 9 1 2 0
4 | 8 4 7 9 6 5 3 3 5 6
5 | 2 2 1 7
6 |
7 |
8 | 3
```

(i) Identify and comment on any outliers.

(ii) What was the age of the oldest person whose marriage is included?

(iii) Redraw the stem and leaf diagram with the leaves sorted.

(iv) Stretch the stem and leaf diagram by using steps of five years between the levels rather than ten.

(v) Describe and comment on the distribution.

8 The table below gives the annual rates of inflation for 12 countries in 1992 and 1991.

Country	Inflation, annual change, %	
	1992	1991
UK	4.1	8.9
Australia	1.5	6.9
Belgium	2.3	3.9
Canada	1.6	6.8
France	2.9	3.4
Germany	4.0	2.8
Italy	6.1	6.5
Japan	2.2	3.3
Netherlands	4.1	2.8
Spain	5.5	6.6
Sweden	7.9	10.9
USA	2.6	5.7
OECD	5.6	6.7

(Source: *The Independent on Sunday* 1/3/92)

Copy and complete this back-to-back stem and leaf diagram and comment on your results.

```
    5 | 1  |
      | 2  |
      | 3  |
    1 | 4  |
      | 5  |
      | 6  | 9
      | 7  |
      | 8  | 9
      | 9  |
      | 10 |
```

Categorical or qualitative data

Chapter 2 will deal in more detail with ways of displaying data. The remainder of this chapter looks at types of data and the basic analysis of numerical data.

Some data come to you in classes or categories. Such data, like these for the members of the Select Committee for Education and Employment, are called categorical or qualitative.

L L L C L   L L L C L   LD C L L C   L LD

C = Conservative; L = Labour; LD = Liberal Democrat
Members are listed alphabetically.
(Source: *www.parliament.uk* August 1999)

Most of the data you encounter, however, will be numerical data (also called quantitative data).

Numerical or quantitative data

VARIABLE

The score you get when you throw an ordinary die is one of the values 1, 2, 3, 4, 5 or 6. Rather than repeatedly using the phrase 'The score you get when you throw an ordinary die', statisticians find it convenient to use a capital letter, *X*, say. They let *X* stand for 'The score you get when you throw an ordinary die' and because this varies, *X* is referred to as a *variable*.

Similarly, if you are collecting data and this involves, for example, noting the temperature in classrooms at noon, then you could let *T* stand for 'the temperature in a classroom at noon'. So *T* is another example of a variable.

RANDOM VARIABLE

If a variable has an associated *probability*, such as when throwing an ordinary die the probability of getting a 6 is $\frac{1}{6}$, then the variable is referred to as a *random variable*.

It is possible to record most data as values of a *variable*, for example, people's heights or weights, or the score on a die. In such cases, the classification is done on the basis of a number, rather than a description, and the data are *numerical* or *quantitative*. Numerical or quantitative data are either *discrete* or *continuous*.

Discrete and continuous variables

The scores on a die, 1, 2, 3, 4, 5 and 6, the number of goals a football team scores, 0, 1, 2, 3, ... and British shoe sizes 1, $1\frac{1}{2}$, 2, $2\frac{1}{2}$, ... are all examples of *discrete variables*. What they have in common is that all possible values can be listed.

Distance, mass, temperature and speed are all examples of continuous variables. Continuous variables, if measured accurately enough, can take any appropriate value. You cannot list all possible values.

You have already seen the example of age. This is rather a special case. It is nearly always given rounded down (i.e. truncated). Although your age changes continuously every moment of your life, you actually state it in steps of one year, in completed years, and not to the nearest whole year. So a man who is a few days short of his 20th birthday will still say he is 19.

In practice, data for a continuous variable are always given in a rounded form.

- A person's height, h, given as 168 cm, measured to the nearest centimetre; $167.5 \leqslant h < 168.5$
- A temperature, T, given as 21.8 °C, measured to the nearest tenth of a degree; $21.75 \leqslant T < 21.85$
- The depth of an ocean, d, is given as 9200 m, measured to the nearest 100 m; $9150 \leqslant d < 9250$

Notice the rounding convention here: if a figure is on the borderline it is rounded up. There are other rounding conventions.

Measures of central tendency

When describing a typical value to represent a data set most people think of a value at the centre and use the word *average*. When using the word average they are often referring to the *arithmetic mean*, which is usually just called the *mean* and when asked to explain how to get the mean most people respond by saying 'add up the data values and divide by the total number of data values'.

There are actually several different averages and so, in statistics, it is important for you to be more precise about the *average* to which you are referring. Before looking at the different types of average or *measure of central tendency*, you need to be familiar with some notation.

Σ notation and the mean, $\bar{x}$

A sample of size n taken from a population can be identified as follows:

The first item can be called x_1, the second item x_2 and so on up to x_n.

The sum of these n items of data is given by $x_1 + x_2 + x_3 + \cdots + x_n$.

A shorthand for this is $\sum_{i=1}^{i=n} x_i$ or $\sum_{i=1}^{n} x_i$. This is read as the sum of all the terms x_i when i equals 1 to n.

So $\qquad \sum_{i=1}^{n} x_i = x_1 + x_2 + x_3 + \cdots + x_n.$ $\qquad$ ⌡ Σ is the Greek letter, sigma ⌠

If there is no ambiguity about the number of items of data, the subscripts i can be dropped and $\sum_{i=1}^{n} x_i$ becomes Σx.

Σx is read as 'sigma x' meaning 'the sum of all the x items'.

The mean of these n items of data is written as $\bar{x} = \dfrac{x_1 + x_2 + x_3 + \cdots + x_n}{n}$

where $\bar{x}$ is the symbol for the mean, referred to as 'x-bar'.

It is usual to write $\bar{x} = \dfrac{\Sigma x}{n}$ or $\bar{x} = \dfrac{1}{n}\Sigma x$.

This is a formal way of writing 'To get the mean you add up all the data values and divide by the total number of data values'.

Often data is presented in a frequency table. The notation for the mean is slightly different in such cases.

Alex is a member of the local bird-watching group. The group are concerned about the effect of pollution and climatic change on the well-being of birds. One spring Alex surveyed a sample of woodlands and domestic garden sites for Blue Tit nests. Blue Tits usually lay 1–5 eggs. Alex collected data from 50 nests. His data are shown in the following frequency table.

Number of eggs, x	Frequency, f
1	4
2	12
3	9
4	18
5	7
	$\Sigma f = 50$

> This represents 'the sum of the separate frequencies is 50'. That is, $4 + 12 + 9 + 18 + 7 = 50$

It would be possible to write out the data set in full as $1, 1, 1, \ldots, 5, 5$ and then calculate the mean as before. However, it would not be sensible and in practice the mean is calculated as follows:

$$\bar{x} = \frac{1 \times 4 + 2 \times 12 + 3 \times 9 + 4 \times 18 + 5 \times 7}{50}$$

$$= \frac{162}{50} = 3.24$$

> This represents the sum of each of the x terms multiplied by its frequency

In general, this is written as $\boxed{\bar{x} = \dfrac{\Sigma xf}{n}}$

> $n = \Sigma f$

In the survey at the beginning of this chapter the mean of the cyclists' ages, $\bar{x} = \frac{2717}{91} = 29.9$ years.

However, a mean of the ages needs to be adjusted because age is always rounded down. For example, John Smith gave his age as 45. He could be exactly 45 years old or possibly his 46th birthday may be one day away. So, each of the people in the sample could be from 0 to almost a year older than their quoted age. To adjust for this discrepancy you need to add 0.5 years on to the average of 29.9 to give 30.4 years.

Note

The mean is the most commonly used average in statistics. The mean described here is correctly called the *arithmetic mean*; there are other forms, for example, the geometric mean, harmonic mean and weighted mean, all of which have particular applications.

The mean is used when the total quantity is also of interest. For example, the staff at the water treatment works for a city would be interested in the mean amount of water used per household ($\bar{x}$) but would also need to know the total amount of water used in the city (Σx). The mean can give a misleading result if exceptionally large or exceptionally small values occur in the data set.

There are two other commonly used statistical measures of a typical (or representative) value of a data set. These are the median and the mode. A fourth measure is the mid-range.

Median

The median is the value of the middle item when all the data items are ranked in order. If there are n items of data then the median is the value of the $\frac{n+1}{2}$ th item.

If n is odd then there is a middle value and this is the median. In the survey of the cyclists we have

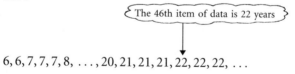

The 46th item of data is 22 years

$$6, 6, 7, 7, 7, 8, \ldots, 20, 21, 21, 21, 22, 22, 22, \ldots$$

So for the ages of the 91 cyclists, the median is the age of the $\frac{91+1}{2} = 46$th person and this is 22 years.

If n is even and the two middle values are a and b then the median is $\frac{a+b}{2}$. For example, if the reporter had not noticed that 138 was invalid there would have been 92 items of data. Then the median age for the cyclists would be found as follows.

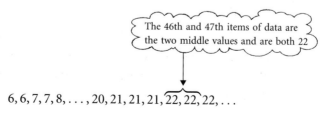

The 46th and 47th items of data are the two middle values and are both 22

$$6, 6, 7, 7, 8, \ldots, 20, 21, 21, 21, \overbrace{22, 22}, 22, \ldots$$

So the median age for the cyclists is given as the mean of the 46th and 47th items of data. That is, $\frac{22+22}{2} = 22$.

It is a coincidence that the median turns out to be the same. However, what is important to notice is that an extreme value has little or no effect on the value of the median. The median is said to be resistant to outliers.

The *median* is easy to work out if the data are already ranked, otherwise it can be tedious. However, with the increased availability of computers, it is easier to sort data and so the use of the median is increasing. Illustrating data on a stem and leaf diagram orders the data and makes it easy to identify the median. The median usually provides a good representative value and, as seen above, it is not affected by extreme values. It is particularly useful if some values are missing; for example, if 50 people took part in a cross country race then the median is halfway between the 25th and 26th values. If some people failed to complete the course the mean would be impossible to calculate, but the median is easy to find.

In finding an *average* salary the median is often a more appropriate measure than the mean since a few people earning very large salaries would have a big effect on the mean but not on the median.

Mode

The *mode* is the value which occurs most frequently. If two non-adjacent values occur more frequently than the rest, the distribution is said to be *bimodal*, even if the frequencies are not the same for both modes.

Bimodal data usually indicates that the sample has been taken from two populations. For example, a sample of students' heights (male and female) would probably be bimodal reflecting the different average heights of males and females.

For the cyclists' ages, the mode is 9 years (the frequency is 6).

For a small set of discrete data the mode can often be misleading, especially if there are many values the data can take. Several items of data can happen to fall on a particular value. The mode is used when the most probable or most frequently occurring value is of interest. For example, a dress shop manager who is considering stocking a new style would first buy dresses of the new style in the modal size, as she would be most likely to sell those ones.

Mid-range

The *mid-range* is the value midway between the upper extreme and the lower extreme values in the data set.

For the cyclists' ages the mid-range is $\frac{(6+88)}{2} = 47$ years.

The mid-range is easy to calculate but only useful if the data are reasonably symmetrical and free from outliers; for example, ages of students in a school class. A single outlier can have a major effect on the mid-range; for example, the mid-range of the cyclists' ages is increased by ten years by the inclusion of the 88-year-old, Millie Smith. By comparison, the mean is increased by 0.6 years, the mode and the median remain unchanged.

Which average you use will depend on the particular data you have and on what you are trying to find out.

The measures for the cyclists' ages are summarised below.

Mean   29.9 years   (adjusted = 30.4 years)
Mode   9 years
Median   22 years
Mid-range   47 years

 Which do you think is most representative?

EXERCISE 1B

1   Find the mode, mean, mid-range and median of these figures:

(i)   23 46 45 45 29   51 36 41 37 47   45 44 41 31 33

(ii)   110 111 116 119 129   126 132 116 122 130
      116 132 118 122 127   132 126 138 117 111

(iii) 5 7 7 9 1   2 3 5 6 6   8 6 5 7 9   2 2 5 6 6
      6 4 7 7 6   1 3 3 5 7   8 2 8 7 6   5 4 3 6 7

2   For each of these sets of data
   (a) find the mode, mean, mid-range and median
   (b) state, with reasons, which you consider to be the most appropriate form of average to describe the distribution.

(i)   The ages of students in a class in years and months:

     14.1 14.11 14.5 14.6 14.0   14.7 14.7 14.9 14.1   14.2
     14.6 14.5   14.8 14.2 14.0   14.9 14.2 14.8 14.11 14.8
     15.0 14.7   14.8 14.9 14.3   14.5 14.4 14.3 14.6   14.1

(ii)   The shoe sizes of children in a class:

     3 $2\frac{1}{2}$ 5 4 $3\frac{1}{2}$ 4 4 4 $2\frac{1}{2}$ 6 $4\frac{1}{2}$ 5 $5\frac{1}{2}$ 4 $3\frac{1}{2}$
     $1\frac{1}{2}$ 3   3 4 $2\frac{1}{2}$ $3\frac{1}{2}$ 5 4 3 $4\frac{1}{2}$ $3\frac{1}{2}$ 4 5 $3\frac{1}{2}$ $4\frac{1}{2}$

(iii) The number of pints of beer drunk by people in *The Crown and Anchor* one Friday evening:

     4 0 0 0 $\frac{1}{2}$ 5 3 4 0 0 $1\frac{1}{2}$ 0 4 8 0
     4 4 $\frac{1}{2}$ 0 6   3 3 4 5 4 $\frac{1}{2}$ 3 0 4 4

(iv) Students' marks on an examination paper:

55 78 45 54 0   62 43 56 71 65   0 67 75 51 100
39 45 66 71 52   71 0 0 59 61   56 59 64 57 63

(v) The scores of a cricketer during a season's matches:

10 23 65 0 1   24 47 2 21 53   5 4 23 169 21
17 34 33 21 0   10 78 1 56 3   2 0 128 12 19

(vi) Scores when a die is thrown 40 times:

2 4 5 5 1   3 4 6 2 5   2 4 6 1 2   5 4 4 1 1
3 4 6 5 5   2 3 3 1 6   5 4 2 1 3   3 2 1 6 6

Frequency distributions

You will often have to deal with data that are presented in a frequency table. Frequency tables summarise the data and also allow you to get an idea of the shape of the distribution.

EXAMPLE 1.1

Claire runs a fairground stall. She has designed a game where customers pay £1 and are given 10 marbles which they have to try to get into a container 4 metres away. If they get more than 8 in the container they win £5. Before introducing the game to the customers she tries it out on a sample of 50 people. The number of successes scored by each person is noted.

5 7 8 7 5 4 0 9 10 6
4 8 8 9 5 6 3 2 4 4
6 5 5 7 6 7 5 6 9 2
7 7 6 3 5 5 6 9 8 7
5 2 1 6 8 5 4 4 3 3

The data are discrete. They have not been organised in any way, so they are referred to as raw data.

Calculate the mode, median, mid-range and mean scores. Comment on your results.

SOLUTION

The *frequency distribution* of these data can be illustrated in a table. The number of 0s, 1s, 2s, etc. are counted to give the frequency of each mark.

Score	Frequency
0	1
1	1
2	3
3	4
4	6
5	10
6	8
7	7
8	5
9	4
10	1
Total	50

With the data presented in this form it is easier to find or calculate the different averages.

The mode score is 5 (frequency 10).

As the number of items of data is even, the distribution has two middle values, the 25th and 26th scores. From the distribution, by adding up the frequencies, it can be seen that the 25th score is 5 and the 26th score is 6. Consequently the median score is $\frac{1}{2}(5 + 6) = 5.5$.

The mid-range score is $\frac{1}{2}(0 + 10) = 5$.

Representing a score by x and its frequency by f, the calculation of the mean is shown in this table.

Score, x	Frequency, f	$x \times f$
0	1	$0 \times 1 = 0$
1	1	$1 \times 1 = 1$
2	3	$2 \times 3 = 6$
3	4	12
4	6	24
5	10	50
6	8	48
7	7	49
8	5	40
9	4	36
10	1	10
	$\sum f = 50$	$\sum xf = 276$

So
$$\bar{x} = \frac{\sum xf}{n}$$

$$= \frac{276}{50} = 5.52$$

The values of the mode (5), the median (5.5), the mean (5.52) and the mid-range (5) are close. This is because the distribution of scores does not have any extreme values and is reasonably symmetrical.

1 A bag contained six counters numbered 1, 2, 3, 4, 5 and 6. A counter was drawn from the bag, its number was noted and then it was returned to the bag. This was repeated 100 times. The results were recorded in a table giving the frequency distribution shown.

Number, x	Frequency, f
1	15
2	25
3	16
4	20
5	13
6	11

(i) State the mode.

(ii) Find the median.

(iii) Calculate the mid-range.

(iv) Calculate the mean.

2 A sample of 50 boxes of matches with stated contents 40 matches was taken. The actual number of matches in each box was recorded. The resulting frequency distribution is shown in the table.

Number of matches, x	Frequency, f
37	5
38	5
39	10
40	8
41	7
42	6
43	5
44	4

(i) State the mode.

(ii) Find the median.

(iii) Calculate the mid-range.

(iv) Calculate the mean.

(v) State, with reasons, which you think is the most appropriate form of average to describe the distribution.

3 A survey of the number of students in 80 classrooms in Avonford College was carried out. The data were recorded in a table as follows.

Number of students, x	Frequency, f
5	1
11	1
15	6
16	9
17	12
18	16
19	18
20	13
21	3
22	1
	$\sum f = 80$

(i) State the mode.

(ii) Find the median.

(iii) Calculate the mid-range.

(iv) Calculate the mean.

(v) State, with reasons, which you think is the most appropriate form of average to describe the distribution.

4 The tally below gives the scores of the football teams in the matches of the 1982 World Cup finals.

```
 0   HHT HHT HHT HHT HHT HHT I
 1   HHT HHT HHT HHT HHT HHT HHT III
 2   HHT HHT HHT I
 3   HHT III
 4   HHT I
 5   II
 6
 7
 8
 9
10   I
```

(i) Find the mode, mean, mid-range and median of this data.

(ii) State which of these you think is the most representative measure.

5 The vertical line chart below shows the number of times the various members of a school year had to take their driving test before passing it.

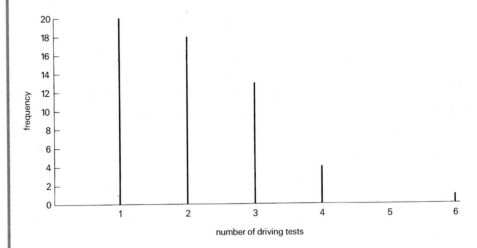

(i) Find the mode, mean, mid-range and median of these data.

(ii) State which of these you think is the most representative measure.

Grouped data

Grouping means putting the data into a number of classes. The number of data items falling into any class is called the *frequency* for that class.

When numerical data are grouped, each item of data falls within a *class interval* lying between *class boundaries*.

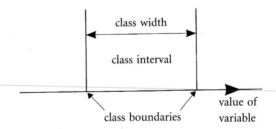

Figure 1.8

You must always be careful about the choice of class boundaries because it must be absolutely clear to which class any item belongs. A form with the following wording:

How old are you? Please tick one box.

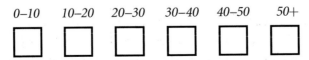

would cause problems. A ten-year-old could tick either of the first two boxes.

A better form of wording would be:

How old are you (in completed years)? Please tick one box.

0–9   10–19   20–29   30–39   40–49   50+

☐ ☐ ☐ ☐ ☐ ☐

Notice that this says 'in completed years'. Otherwise a $9\frac{1}{2}$-year-old might not know which of the first two boxes to tick.

Another way of writing this is:

$$0 \leqslant A < 10 \quad 10 \leqslant A < 20 \quad 20 \leqslant A < 30$$
$$30 \leqslant A < 40 \quad 40 \leqslant A < 50 \quad 50 \leqslant A$$

Even somebody aged 9 years and 364 days would clearly still come in the first group.

? Another way of writing these classes, which you will sometimes see, is

$$0-, 10-, 20-, \ldots, 50-.$$

What is the disadvantage of this way?

Working with grouped data

There is often a good reason for grouping raw data.

- There may be a lot of data.
- The data may be spread over a wide range.
- Most of the values collected may be different.

Whatever the reason, grouping data should make it easier to analyse and present a summary of findings, whether in a table or in a diagram.

For some *discrete data* it may not be necessary or desirable to group them. For example, a survey of the number of passengers in cars using a busy road is unlikely to produce many integer values outside the range 0 to 4 (not counting the driver). However, there are cases when grouping the data (or perhaps constructing a stem and leaf diagram) are an advantage.

Discrete data

At various times during one week the number of cars passing a survey point were noted. Each item of data relates to the number of cars passing during a five-minute period. A hundred such periods were surveyed. The data is summarised in the following frequency table.

Number of cars, x	Frequency, f
0–9	5
10–19	8
20–29	13
30–39	20
40–49	22
50–59	21
60–70	11

$$\sum f = 100$$

From the frequency table you can see there is a slight negative (or left) skew.

ESTIMATING THE MEAN

When data are grouped the individual values are lost. This is not often a serious problem; as long as the data are reasonably distributed throughout each interval it is possible to *estimate* statistics such as the mean, knowing that your answers will be reasonably accurate.

To estimate the mean you first assume that all the values in an interval are equally spaced about a mid-point. The mid-points are taken as representative values of the intervals.

The mid-value for the interval 0–9 is $\dfrac{0 + 9}{2} = 4.5$.

The mid-value for the interval 10–19 is $\dfrac{10 + 19}{2} = 14.5$, and so on.

The $x \times f$ column can now be added to the frequency distribution table and an estimate for the mean found.

Number of cars, x (mid-values)	Frequency, f	$x \times f$
4.5	5	$4.5 \times 5 = 22.5$
14.5	8	$14.5 \times 8 = 116.0$
24.5	13	318.5
34.5	20	690.0
44.5	22	979.0
54.5	21	1144.5
65.0	11	715.0

$$\sum f = 100 \qquad \sum xf = 3985.5$$

The mean is given by

$$\bar{x} = \frac{3985.5}{100}$$

$$= 39.855$$

The original raw data, summarised in the above frequency table, is shown below.

10	18	68	67	25	62	49	11	12	8
9	46	53	57	30	63	34	21	68	31
20	16	29	13	31	56	9	34	45	55
35	40	45	48	54	50	34	32	47	60
70	52	21	25	53	41	29	63	43	50
40	48	45	38	51	25	52	55	47	46
46	50	8	25	56	18	20	36	36	9
38	39	53	45	42	42	61	55	30	38
62	47	58	54	59	25	24	53	42	61
18	30	32	45	49	28	31	27	54	38

In this form it is impossible to get an overview of the number of cars, nor would listing every possible value in a frequency table (0 to 70) be helpful.

However, grouping the data and estimating the mean was not the only option. Constructing a stem and leaf diagram and using it to find the median would have been another possibility.

 Is it possible to find estimates for the other measures of centre? Find the mean of the original data and compare it to the estimate.

The data the reporter collected when researching his article on cycling accidents included the distance from home, in metres, of those involved in cycling accidents. In full these were as follows:

3000	75	1200	300	50	10	150	1500	250	25
200	4500	35	60	120	400	2400	140	45	5
1250	3500	30	75	250	1200	250		50	250	450
15	4000								

It is clear that there is considerable spread in the data. It is continuous data and the reporter is aware that they appear to have been rounded but he does not know to what level of precision. Consequently there is no way of reflecting the level of precision in setting the interval boundaries.

The reporter wants to estimate the mean and decides on the following grouping.

Location relative to home	Distance, d, in metres	Distance mid-value, x	Frequency (number of accidents), f	$x \times f$
Very close	$0 \leqslant d < 100$	50	12	600
Close	$100 \leqslant d < 500$	300	11	3300
Not far	$500 \leqslant d < 1500$	1000	3	3000
Quite far	$1500 \leqslant d < 5000$	3250	6	19 500
			$\sum f = 32$	$\sum xf = 26\,400$

$$\bar{x} = \frac{26\,400}{32} = 825 \text{ m}$$

A summary of the measures of centre for the original and grouped accident data is given below.

	Raw data		Grouped data
Mean	$25\,785 \div 32 = 806$ m		825 m
Mode	250 m	Modal group	$0 \leqslant d < 100$ m
Median	$\frac{1}{2}(200 + 250) = 225$ m		
Mid-range	$\frac{1}{2}(5 + 4500) = 2252.5$ m		

 Which measure of centre seems most appropriate for these data?

THE REPORTER'S ARTICLE

The reporter decided that he had enough information and wrote the article below.

THE AVONFORD STAR

A council that does not care

The level of civilisation of any society can be measured by how much it cares for its most vulnerable members.

On that basis our town council rates somewhere between savages and barbarians. Every day they sit back complacently while those least able to defend themselves, the very old and the very young, run the gauntlet of our treacherous streets.

I refer of course to the lack of adequate safety measures for our cyclists, 60% of whom are children or senior citizens. Statistics show that they only have to put one wheel outside their front doors to be in mortal danger. 80% of cycling accidents happen within 1500 metres of home.

Last week Denise Cropper became the latest unwitting addition to these statistics. Luckily she is now on the road to recovery but that is no thanks to the members of our unfeeling council who set people on the road to death and injury without a second thought.

What, this paper asks our councillors, are you doing about providing safe cycle tracks from our housing estates to our schools and shopping centres? And what are you doing to promote safety awareness among our cyclists, young and old?

Answer: Nothing.

Is it a fair article? Is it justified, based on the available evidence?

Continuous data

For a statistics project Robert, a student at Avonford College, collected the heights of 50 female students.

He constructed a frequency table for his project and included the calculations to find an estimate for the mean of his data.

Height, h	Mid-value, x	Frequency, f	xf
$157 < h \leqslant 159$	158	4	632
$159 < h \leqslant 161$	160	11	1760
$161 < h \leqslant 163$	162	19	3078
$163 < h \leqslant 165$	164	8	1312
$165 < h \leqslant 167$	166	5	830
$167 < h \leqslant 169$	168	3	504
		$\sum f = 50$	$\sum xf = 8116$

$$\bar{x} = \frac{8116}{50}$$

$$= 162.32$$

Note: Class boundaries

His teacher was concerned about the class boundaries and asked Robert 'To what degree of accuracy have you recorded your data?' Robert told him 'I rounded all my data to the nearest centimetre'. Robert showed his teacher his raw data.

163	160	167	168	166	164	166	162	163	163
165	163	163	159	159	158	162	163	163	166
164	162	164	160	161	162	162	160	169	162
163	160	167	162	158	161	162	163	165	165
163	163	168	165	165	161	160	161	161	161

Robert's teacher said that the class boundaries should have been

$157.5 \leqslant h < 159.5$

$159.5 \leqslant h < 161.5$, and so on.

He explained that a height recorded to the nearest centimetre as 158 cm has a value in the interval 158 ± 0.5 cm (this can be written as $157.5 \leqslant x < 158.5$). Similarly the actual values of those recorded as 159 cm lie in the interval $158.5 \leqslant x < 159.5$. So, the interval $157.5 \leqslant h < 159.5$ covers the *actual* values of the data items 158 and 159. The interval $159.5 \leqslant h < 161.5$ covers the actual values of 160 and 161 and so on.

? What adjustment does Robert need to make to his estimated mean in the light of his teacher's comments?

Find the mean of the raw data. What do you notice when you compare it with your estimate?

You are not always told the level of precision of summarised data and the class widths are not always equal, as the reporter for the *Avonford Star* discovered. Also, there are different ways of representing class boundaries, as the following example illustrates.

EXAMPLE 1.2 The frequency distribution shows the lengths of telephone calls made by Emily during August. Choose suitable mid-class values and estimate Emily's mean call time for August.

SOLUTION

Time (seconds)	Frequency, f	Mid-value, x	xf
0–	39	30	1170
60–	15	90	1350
120–	12	150	1800
180–	8	240	1920
300–	4	400	1600
500–1000	1	750	750
	$\sum f = 79$		$\sum xf = 8590$

$$\bar{x} = \frac{8590}{79}$$

$$= 108.7 \text{ seconds (3 sf)}$$

Note

1 The interval '0–' can be written as $0 \leqslant x < 60$, the interval '60–' can be written as $60 \leqslant x < 120$, and so on, up to '500–1000' which can be written as $500 \leqslant x \leqslant 1000$.

2 There is no indication of the level of precision of the recorded data. They may have been recorded to the nearest second.

3 The class widths vary.

1 A college nurse keeps a record of the heights, measured to the nearest centimetre, of a group of students she treats.

Her data are summarised in the following grouped frequency table.

Height (cm)	110–119	120–129	130–139	140–149	150–159	160–169	170–179	180–189
Number of students	1	3	10	28	65	98	55	15

Choose suitable mid-class values and calculate an estimate for the mean height.

2 A junior school teacher noted the time to the nearest minute a group of children spent reading during a particular day.

The data are summarised as follows:

Time (nearest minute)	Number of children
20–29	12
30–39	21
40–49	36
50–59	24
60–69	12
70–89	9
90–119	2

(i) Choose suitable mid-class values and calculate an estimate for the mean time spent reading by the pupils.

(ii) Some time later, the teacher collected similar data from a group of 25 children from a neigbouring school. She calculated the mean to be 75.5 minutes. Compare the estimate you obtained in part (i) with this value.

What assumptions must you make for the comparison to be meaningful?

3 The stated age of the 91 cyclists considered earlier is summarised by the following grouped frequency distribution.

Stated age (years)	Frequency
0–9	13
10–19	26
20–29	16
30–39	10
40–49	6
50–59	5
60–69	14
70–79	0
80–89	1
	$\sum f = 91$

(i) Choose suitable mid-interval values and calculate an estimate of the mean stated age.

(ii) Make a suitable error adjustment to your answer to part (i) to give an estimate of the mean age of the cyclists.

(iii) The adjusted mean of the actual data was 30.4 years. Compare this with your answer to part (ii) and comment.

4 In an agricultural experiment, 320 plants were grown on a plot. The lengths of the stems were measured, to the nearest centimetre, 10 weeks after planting. The lengths were found to be distributed as in the following table:

Length, x (cm)	Frequency (number of plants)
$20.5 \leqslant x < 32.5$	30
$32.5 \leqslant x < 38.5$	80
$38.5 \leqslant x < 44.5$	90
$44.5 \leqslant x < 50.5$	60
$50.5 \leqslant x < 68.5$	60

Calculate an estimate of the mean of stem lengths from this experiment.

5 The reporter of the *Avonford Star* considered choosing different classes for the data dealing with the cyclists who were involved in accidents.

He summarised the distances from home of the 91 cyclists as follows:

Distance, d (metres)	Frequency
$0 \leqslant d < 50$	7
$50 \leqslant d < 100$	5
$100 \leqslant d < 150$	2
$150 \leqslant d < 200$	1
$200 \leqslant d < 300$	5
$300 \leqslant d < 500$	3
$500 \leqslant d < 1000$	0
$1000 \leqslant d < 5000$	9

$$\sum f = 32$$

(i) Choose suitable class mid-values and estimate the mean.

(ii) The mean of the raw data is 806 m and his previous grouping gave an estimate for the mean of 825 m. Compare your answer to this value and comment.

6 A case containing 270 oranges was opened and each orange was weighed. The masses, given to the nearest gram, were grouped and the resulting distribution is as follows:

Mass, x (grams)	Frequency (number of oranges)
60–99	20
100–119	60
120–139	80
140–159	50
160–220	60

(i) State the class boundaries for the interval 60–99.

(ii) Calculate an estimate for the mean mass of the oranges from the crate.

Measures of spread

In the last section you saw how an estimate for the mean can be found from grouped data. The mean is just one example of a *typical value* of a data set. You also saw how the mode and the median can be found from small data sets. The next chapter considers the use of the median as a *typical value* when dealing with grouped data and also the *interquartile range* as a *measure of spread*. In this chapter we will consider the range, the mean absolute deviation, the variance and the standard deviation as measures of spread.

Range

The simplest measure of spread is the *range*. This is just the difference between the largest value in the data set (the upper extreme) and the smallest value (the lower extreme).

> *Range = largest − smallest*

The figures below are the prices, in pence, of a 100 g jar of *Nesko* coffee in ten different shops:

    161   161   163   163   167   168   170   172   172   172

The range for this data is

    Range $= 172 - 161 = 11$p.

⚠ Be careful not to confuse the range, a measure of spread, with the mid-range, a measure of central tendency.

The mid-range for these data is $\frac{161+172}{2} = 166.5$p.

EXAMPLE 1.3

Ruth is investigating the amount of money students at Avonford College earn from part-time work on one particular weekend. She collects and orders data from two classes and this is shown below.

Class 1									
10	10	10	10	10	10	12	15	15	15
16	16	16	16	18	18	20	25	38	90

Class 2									
10	10	10	10	10	10	12	12	12	12
15	15	15	15	16	17	18	19	20	20
25	35	35							

She calculates the mean amount earned for each class. Her results are

Class 1: $\bar{x}_1 = £19.50$
Class 2: $\bar{x}_2 = £16.22$

She concludes that the students in Class 1 each earn about £3 more, on average, than do the students in Class 2.

Her teacher suggests she look at the spread of the data. What further information does this reveal?

SOLUTION

Ruth calculates the range for each class: Range (Class 1) = £80
Range (Class 2) = £25

She concludes that the part-time earnings in Class 1 are much more spread out.

However, when Ruth looks again at the raw data she notices that one student in Class 1 earned £90, considerably more than anybody else. If that item of data is ignored then the spread of data for the two classes is similar.

⚠ One of the problems with the range is that it is prone to the effect of extreme values.

❓ Calculate the mean earnings of Class 1 with the item £90 removed.

What can you conclude about the effect of extreme values on the mean?

The range does not use all of the available information; only the extreme values are used. In quality control this can be an advantage as it is very sensitive to something going wrong on a production line. Also the range is easy to calculate.

However, usually we want a measure of spread that uses all the available data and that relates to a central value.

The mean absolute deviation

Kim and Joe play as strikers for two of Avonford's local football teams. They are hoping to be picked for the Avonford Town team who are due to play nearby Newton St Mary's in a friendly match. The team manager is considering their scoring records.

Kim's scoring record over ten matches looks like this:

$$0 \quad 1 \quad 0 \quad 3 \quad 0 \quad 2 \quad 0 \quad 0 \quad 0 \quad 4$$

Joe's record looks like this:

$$1 \quad 1 \quad 1 \quad 0 \quad 0 \quad 2 \quad 1 \quad 1 \quad 2 \quad 2$$

The mean scores are, for Kim, $\bar{x}_1 = 1$ and, for Joe, $\bar{x}_2 = 1.1$.

Looking first at Kim's data consider the differences, or *deviations*, of his scores from the mean.

Number of goals scored, x	0	1	0	3	0	2	0	0	0	4
Deviations $(x-\bar{x})$	-1	0	-1	2	-1	1	-1	-1	-1	3

To find a summary measure you need to combine the deviations in some way. If you just add them together they total zero.

 Why does the sum of the deviations always total zero?

The mean absolute deviation ignores the signs and adds together the *absolute deviations*. The symbol $|d|$ tells you to take the positive, or absolute, value of d.

For example $|-2| = 2$ and $|2| = 2$.

It is now possible to sum the deviations

$$1 + 0 + 1 + 2 + 1 + 1 + 1 + 1 + 1 + 3 = 12,$$
the *total of the absolute deviations*.

It is important that any measure of spread is not linked to the sample size so you have to average out this total by dividing by the sample size.

In this case the sample size is 10. The *mean absolute deviation* $= \frac{12}{10} = 1.2$.

> The mean absolute deviation from the mean $= \dfrac{1}{n} \sum |x - \bar{x}|$

For Joe's data the mean absolute deviation is

$$\tfrac{1}{10}\,(0.1+0.1+0.1+1.1+1.1+0.9+0.1+0.1+0.9+0.9)=0.54$$

The average number of goals scored by Kim and Joe is similar (1.0 and 1.1) but Joe is less variable (or more consistent) in his goal scoring (0.54 compared to 1.2).

The mean absolute deviation is an acceptable measure of spread but is not widely used because it is difficult to work with. The *standard deviation* is more important mathematically and is more extensively used.

The variance and standard deviation

An alternative to ignoring the signs is to square the differences or deviations. This gives rise to a measure of spread called the *variance*, which when square-rooted gives the *standard deviation*.

Though not as easy to calculate as the absolute mean deviation, the standard deviation has an important role in the study of more advanced statistics.

To find the variance of a data set | For Kim's data this is:

- Square the deviations $(x-\bar{x})^2$ $(0-1)^2, (1-1)^2, (0-1)^2$, etc.
- Sum the squared deviations $\sum (x-\bar{x})^2$ $1+0+1+4+1+1+1$
$$+1+1+9=20$$

- Find their mean $\dfrac{1}{n}\sum (x-\bar{x})^2$ $\dfrac{1}{10}\times 20=2$

This is known as the *variance*.

$$\text{variance} = \frac{1}{n}\sum (x-\bar{x})^2.$$

The square root of the variance is called the *standard deviation*.

$$sd = \sqrt{\frac{1}{n}\sum (x-\bar{x})^2}$$

So, for Kim's data the variance is 2, but what are the units? In calculating the variance the data are squared. In order to get a measure of spread that has the same units as the original data it is necessary to take the square root of the variance. The resulting statistical measure is known as the *standard deviation*.

 The calculation is often carried out using $n-1$ rather than n as the divisor. In this case the answer is denoted by s.

$$s = \sqrt{\frac{1}{n-1}\sum (x-\bar{x})^2}$$

So for Kim's data the variance is 2, *sd* is $\sqrt{2}=1.41$ and $s=1.49$ goals (3 sf).

This example, using Joe's data, shows how the variance and standard deviation are calculated when the data are given in a frequency table. We've already calculated the mean; $\bar{x}=1.1$.

Number of goals scored, x	Frequency f	Deviation $(x - \bar{x})$	Deviation^2 $(x - \bar{x})^2$	Deviation$^2 \times f$ $[(x - \bar{x})^2 f]$
0	2	$0 - 1.1 = -1.1$	1.21	$1.21 \times 2 = 2.42$
1	5	$1 - 1.1 = -0.1$	0.01	$0.01 \times 5 = 0.05$
2	3	$2 - 1.1 = 0.9$	0.81	$0.81 \times 3 = 2.43$
	$\sum f = 10$			$\sum (x - \bar{x})^2 f = 4.90$

The variance $= \frac{4.90}{10} = 0.49$. For data presented in this way,

the sample variance $= \dfrac{1}{n} \sum (x - \bar{x})^2 f$.

The standard deviation for Joe's data is $s = \sqrt{0.49} = 0.7$ goals.

Comparing this to the standard deviation of Kim's data (1.41), we see that Joe's goal scoring is more consistent (or less variable) than Kim's. This confirms what was found when the mean absolute deviation was calculated for each data set. Joe was found to be a more consistent scorer (mean absolute deviation $= 0.54$) than Kim (mean absolute deviation $= 1.2$).

An alternative form for the variance

The arithmetic involved in calculating $\sum (x - \bar{x})^2 f$ can often be very messy.

An alternative formula for calculating the variance is given by

$$\dfrac{1}{n} \sum x^2 f - \bar{x}^2.$$

Consider Joe's data one more time.

Number of goals scored, x	Frequency f	xf	$x^2 f$
0	2	0	0
1	5	5	5
2	3	6	12
	$\sum f = 10$	$\sum xf = 11$	$\sum x^2 f = 17$

$$\bar{x} = \frac{11}{10} = 1.1 \qquad \text{variance} = \frac{1}{10} \times 17 - 1.1^2$$
$$= 1.7 - 1.21$$
$$= 0.49$$

This gives the same result as using $\dfrac{1}{n} \sum (x - \bar{x})^2 f$. The derivation of this alternative form for the variance is given in the appendix on page 176.

In practice you will make extensive use of your calculator's statistical functions to find the mean and standard deviation of sets of data.

Care should be taken as the notations S, s, sd, σ, and $\hat{\sigma}$ are used differently by different calculator manufacturers, authors and users.

The following examples involve finding or using the sample variance.

EXAMPLE 1.4

The following information relates to a sample of size 60.

$\Sigma x^2 = 18\,000$, $\Sigma x = 960$. Find the mean and the standard deviation.

SOLUTION

$$\bar{x} = \frac{\Sigma x}{n} = \frac{960}{60} = 16$$

$$\text{variance} = \frac{1}{n}\Sigma x^2 - \bar{x}^2 = \frac{18\,000}{60} - 16^2 = 44$$

standard deviation $= \sqrt{44} = 6.63$ (3 sf).

EXAMPLE 1.5

The following information relates to a sample of size 60.

$\Sigma(x - \bar{x})^2 = 2000$, $\Sigma x = 960$. Find the mean and the standard deviation.

SOLUTION

$$\bar{x} = \frac{960}{60} = 16$$

$$\text{variance} = \frac{1}{n}\Sigma(x - \bar{x})^2 = \frac{2000}{60} = 33.3\ldots$$

standard deviation $= \sqrt{33.3\ldots} = 5.77$ (3 sf).

EXAMPLE 1.6

As part of her job as quality controller, Stella collected data relating to the life expectancy of a sample of 60 light bulbs produced by her company. The mean life was 650 hours and the standard deviation was 8 hours. A second sample of 80 bulbs was taken by Sol and resulted in a mean life of 660 hours and standard deviation 7 hours.

Find the overall mean and standard deviation.

SOLUTION

Overall mean:

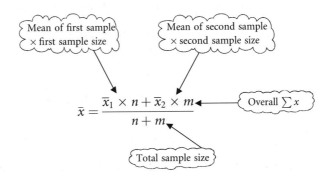

$$\bar{x} = \frac{650 \times 60 + 660 \times 80}{60 + 80}$$

$$= \frac{91\,800}{140} = 655.71\ldots$$

$$= 656 \text{ hours (3 sf)}$$

For Stella's sample the variance is 8^2. Therefore $8^2 = \dfrac{\sum x_1^2}{60} - 650^2$.

For Sol's sample the variance is 7^2. Therefore $7^2 = \dfrac{\sum x_2^2}{80} - 660^2$.

From the above Stella found that $\sum x_1^2 = (8^2 + 650^2) \times 60 = 25\,353\,840$ and $\sum x_2^2 = 34\,851\,920$.

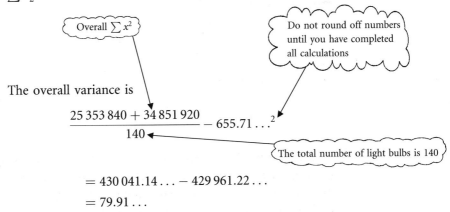

The overall variance is

$$\frac{25\,353\,840 + 34\,851\,920}{140} - 655.71\ldots^2$$

$$= 430\,041.14\ldots - 429\,961.22\ldots$$

$$= 79.91\ldots$$

The overall standard deviation is $\sqrt{79.91\ldots} = 8.94$ hours (3 sf).

❓ Carry out the above calculation using rounded numbers. That is, use 656 for the overall mean rather than 655.71 ... What do you notice?

The standard deviation and outliers

Data sets may contain extreme values and when this occurs you are faced with the problem of how to deal with them.

Many data sets are samples drawn from parent populations which are normally distributed. In these cases approximately:

- 68% of the values lie within 1 standard deviation of the mean
- 95% lie within 2 standard deviations of the mean
- 99.75% lie within 3 standard deviations of the mean.

You will learn more about the normal distribution in *Statistics 2*. If a particular value is *more than two standard deviations from the mean* it should be investigated as possibly not belonging to the data set. If it is as much as three standard deviations or more from the mean then the case to investigate it is even stronger.

 The 2-standard-deviation test should not be seen as a way of defining outliers. It is only a way of identifying those values which it might be worth looking at more closely.

In an A level German class the examination marks at the end of the year are shown below.

$$35 \quad 52 \quad 55 \quad 61 \quad 96 \quad 63 \quad 50 \quad 58 \quad 58 \quad 49 \quad 61$$

The value 96 was thought to be significantly greater than the other values. The mean and standard deviation of the data are $\bar{x} = 58$ and $sd = 14.2$. The value 96 is more than two standard deviations above the mean:

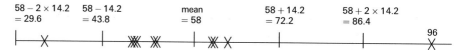

Figure 1.9

When investigated further it turned out that the mark of 96 was achieved by a German boy whose family had moved to Britain and who had taken A level German because he wanted to study German at university. It might be appropriate to omit this value from the data set.

 Calculate the mean and standard deviation of the data with the value 96 left out. Investigate the value using your new mean and standard deviation.

The times taken, in minutes, for some train journeys between Hereford and Shrewsbury were recorded as shown.

$$56 \quad 61 \quad 57 \quad 55 \quad 58 \quad 57 \quad 5 \quad 60 \quad 61 \quad 59$$

It is unnecessary here to calculate the mean standard deviation. The value 5 minutes is obviously a mistake and should be omitted unless it is possible to correct it by referring to the original source of data.

EXERCISE 1E

1 **(i)** Find the mean of the following data.

0 0 0 1 1 1 1 1 2 2 2 2 2 2 2 3 3 3 3 4 4 4 4 4 5 5

(ii) Find the standard deviation using both forms of the formula.

2 Find the mean and standard deviation of the following data.

x	3	4	5	6	7	8	9
f	2	5	8	14	9	4	3

3 Steve Race and Roy Bull are players with the football team Avonford Town. In the 30 games played so far this season their scoring record is as follows.

Goals scored	0	1	2	3	4
Frequency (Steve)	12	8	8	1	1
(Roy)	4	21	5	0	0

(i) Find the mean and the standard deviation of the number of goals each player scored.

(ii) Comment on the players' goal scoring records.

4 For a set of 20 items of data $\sum x = 22$ and $\sum x^2 = 55$. Find the mean and the standard deviation of the data.

5 For a data set of 50 items of data $\sum (x - \bar{x})^2 f = 8$ and $\sum xf = 20$. Find the mean and the standard deviation of the data.

6 Two thermostats were used under identical conditions. The water temperatures, in °C, are given below:

Thermostat A: 24   25   27   23   26
Thermostat B: 26   26   23   22   28

(i) Calculate the mean and standard deviation for each set of water temperatures.

(ii) Which is the better thermostat? Give a reason.

A second sample of data was collected using thermostat A.

25   24   24   25   26   25   24   24

(iii) Find the overall mean and the overall standard deviation for the two sets of data for thermostat A.

7 Mrs Davies has a choice of routes to work. She timed her journey along each route on several occasions and the times in minutes are given below.

Town route: 15   16   20   28   21
Country route: 19   21   20   22   18

(i) Calculate the mean and standard deviation of each set of journey times.
(ii) Which route would you recommend? Give a reason.

8 In a certain district, the mean annual rainfall is 80 cm, with standard deviation 4 cm.
(i)   One year it was 90 cm. Was this an exceptional year?
(ii)   The next year had a total of 78 cm. Was that exceptional?

Jake, a local amateur meteorologist, kept a record of the weekly rainfall in his garden. His first data set, comprising 20 weeks of figures resulted in a mean weekly rainfall of 1.5 cm. The standard deviation was 0.1 cm. His second set of data, over 32 weeks, resulted in a mean of 1.7 cm and a standard deviation of 0.09 cm.
(iii) Calculate the overall mean and the overall standard deviation for the whole year.
(iv) Estimate the annual rainfall in Jake's garden.

9 A farmer expects to harvest a crop of 3.8 tonnes, on average, from each hectare of his land, with standard deviation 0.2 tonnes.

One year there was much more rain than usual and he harvested 4.1 tonnes per hectare.
(i) Was this exceptional?
(ii) Do you think the crop was affected by the unusual weather or was the higher yield part of the variability which always occurs?

10 A machine is supposed to produce ball bearings with a mean diameter of 2.0 mm. A sample of ten ball bearings was taken from the production line and the diameters measured.

The results, in mm, were as follows:

2.0   2.1   2.0   1.8   2.4   2.3   1.9   2.1

(i) Calculate the mean and standard deviation of the diameters.
(ii) Do you think the machine is correctly set?

11 On page 27 you saw the example about Robert, the student at Avonford College, who collected data relating to the heights of female students. This is his corrected frequency table and his calculations so far.

Height, h	Mid-value, x	Frequency, f	xf
$157.5 \leqslant h < 159.5$	158.5	4	634.0
$159.5 \leqslant h < 161.5$	160.5	11	1765.5
$161.5 \leqslant h < 163.5$	162.5	19	3087.5
$163.5 \leqslant h < 165.5$	164.5	8	1316.0
$165.5 \leqslant h < 167.5$	166.5	5	832.5
$167.5 \leqslant h < 169.5$	168.5	3	505.5
		$\sum f = 50$	$\sum xf = 8141.0$

$$\bar{x} = \frac{8141.0}{50} = 162.82$$

(i) Calculate the standard deviation.

Robert's friend Asha collected a sample of heights from 50 male PE students. She calculated the mean and standard deviation to be 170.4 cm and 2.50 cm.

Later on they realised they had excluded two measurements. It was not clear to which of the two data sets, Robert's or Asha's, the two items of data belonged. The values were 171 cm and 166 cm. Robert felt confident about one of the values but not the other.

(ii) Investigate and comment.

12 The table shows the number of club ranking points scored by a bridge player in a series of 30 games.

$$6\ 6\ 3\ 8\ 7\ 9\ 8\ 6\ 5\ 0\ 8\ 7\ 6\ 9\ 8$$
$$6\ 7\ 2\ 8\ 7\ 6\ 6\ 8\ 9\ 7\ 4\ 8\ 7\ 5\ 9$$

Use your calculator to find the mean and standard deviation of these scores.

In a further 20 games, data on the player's scores were summarised by $\sum x = 143$, $\sum x^2 = 1071$. Find the mean and standard deviation of the scores in all 50 games.

[MEI]

13 As part of a biology experiment Andrew caught and weighed 120 minnows. He used his calculator to find the mean and standard deviation of their weights:

Mean   26.231 g
Standard deviation   4.023 g

(i) Find the total weight, $\sum x$, of Andrew's 120 minnows.

(ii) Use the formula standard deviation $= \sqrt{\dfrac{\sum x^2}{n} - \bar{x}^2}$

to find $\sum x^2$ for Andrew's minnows.

Another member of the class, Sharon, did the same experiment with minnows caught from a different stream. Her results are summarised by:

$$n = 80$$
$$\bar{x} = 25.214$$
$$\text{standard deviation} = 3.841$$

Their teacher says they should combine their results into a single set but they have both thrown away their measurements.

(iii) Find n, $\sum x$ and $\sum x^2$ for the combined data set.

(iv) Find the mean and standard deviation for the combined data set.

14 A university admissions officer interviews 30 candidates on Monday and 20 on Tuesday. On each day the mean length of all the interviews is exactly 15 minutes, but the standard deviations are 2 minutes on Monday and $2\frac{1}{2}$ minutes on Tuesday. Find the sums of the squares of the deviations from the mean on each day, and hence find (correct to 1 decimal place) the standard deviation for the two days taken together.

[SMP]

THE AVONFORD STAR

Human computer has it figured

Avonford schoolboy, Simon Newton, astounded his classmates and their parents at a school open evening when he calculated the average of a set of numbers in seconds while everyone else struggled with their adding up.

Mr Truscott, a parent of one of the other children, said, 'I was still looking for my calculator when Simon wrote the answer on the board'.

Simon modestly said when asked about his skill 'It's simply a matter of choosing the most suitable code'.

The *Avonford Star* wants to know 'What is the secret of your code, Simon?'

Without a calculator, see if you can match Simon's performance. The data is repeated below.

Send your result and how you did it into the *Avonford Star*. Don't forget – no calculators!

Number	Frequency
3510	6
3512	4
3514	3
3516	1
3518	2
3520	4

Simon gave a big clue about how he calculated the mean so quickly. He said 'It's simply a matter of choosing the most suitable code'. Simon noticed that subtracting 3510 from each value simplified the data significantly. This is how he did his calculations.

Number, x	Number $- 3510$, y	Frequency, f	$y \times f$
3510	0	6	$0 \times 6 = 0$
3512	2	4	$2 \times 4 = 8$
3514	4	3	$4 \times 3 = 12$
3516	6	1	$6 \times 1 = 6$
3518	8	2	$8 \times 2 = 16$
3520	10	4	$10 \times 4 = 40$
		$\sum f = 20$	$\sum yf = 82$

Average (mean) $= \frac{82}{20} = 4.1$

(3510 is now added back) $3510 + 4.1 = 3514.1$

Linear coding

Simon was using *linear coding* to ease his arithmetic.

Coding is used for two reasons:

(i) to simplify messy arithmetic
(ii) to convert between different units.

Consider again Robert's data on the heights of female students.

Height, h (cm) mid-points	Frequency, f
158.5	4
160.5	11
162.5	19
164.5	8
166.5	5
168.5	3
	$\sum f = 50$

The arithmetic involved in calculating the mean and the standard deviation can be simplified considerably as follows:

The h values are replaced by x values, which are found by

(i) subtracting 158.5 from the h values,

then further simplifying the resulting values, $0, 2, 4, 6, 8$ and 10, by

(ii) dividing by 2, giving $0, 1, 2, 3, 4$ and 5.

Height, h (cm) mid-points	x	Frequency, f	xf	x^2f
158.5	$158.5 - 158.5 = 0 \div 2 = 0$	4	0	0
160.5	$160.5 - 158.5 = 2 \div 2 = 1$	11	11	11
162.5	$162.5 - 158.5 = 4 \div 2 = 2$	19	38	76
164.5	$164.5 - 158.5 = 6 \div 2 = 3$	8	24	72
166.5	4	5	20	80
168.5	5	3	15	75

$$\sum f = 50 \qquad \sum xf = 108 \qquad \sum x^2f = 314$$

$$\bar{x} = \frac{108}{50} = 2.16$$

$$(sd_x)^2 = \frac{314}{50} - 2.16^2 = 1.6144$$

$$sd_x = 1.27 \text{ cm}$$

In this example the data has been *coded* as $x = \dfrac{h - 158.5}{2}$. From this, $h = 2x + 158.5$.

$\therefore \bar{h} = 2\bar{x} + 158.5$ and $sd_h = 2sd_x$.

We can now find the mean and standard deviation of the original data.

$$\bar{h} = 2 \times 2.16 + 158.5 = 162.8 \text{ cm}$$
$$sd_h = 2 \times 1.27 = 2.54 \text{ cm}$$

❓ In the above example could you have subtracted 162.5 rather than 158.5?

The following example illustrates how linear coding can be used to convert between units.

EXAMPLE 1.7   For a period of ten days during August the mean temperature in Gresham, Oregon, was 80° Fahrenheit. The standard deviation during that period (in degrees Fahrenheit) was 0.7 °F. Find the mean temperature and the standard deviation in degrees Celsius.

SOLUTION

The conversion formula is $c = \dfrac{5(f - 32)}{9}$

$\left(\text{which can be written as } c = \dfrac{5f}{9} - \dfrac{160}{9}\right).$

So $\qquad \bar{c} = \dfrac{5 \times 80}{9} - \dfrac{160}{9} = \dfrac{240}{9}$

$\qquad\qquad = 26\tfrac{2}{3}\,°\mathrm{C} \quad \text{or} \quad 26.7\,°\mathrm{C}$

Subtracting 32 does not affect the spread so the standard deviation is

$$sd_c = \tfrac{5}{9} \times sd_f = \dfrac{5 \times 0.7}{9} = 0.4\,°\mathrm{C}$$

The coded values are easy to calculate, even without a calculator!

In general, if the coded value, x, is given by a linear equation (or code) of the form $x = \dfrac{y - a}{b}$, then the original value, y, can be found using the equation $y = a + bx$. And, if $\bar{x}$ and sd_x are the mean and standard deviation of the coded x values, then $\bar{y}$ and sd_y, the mean and the standard deviation of the original data, the y values, can be found using $\bar{y} = a + b\bar{x}$ and $sd_y = bsd_x$.

❓ Look back at Robert's data on the heights of female students and check that Robert used $a = 158.5$ and $b = 2$ to code his data.

1 Calculate the mean and standard deviation of the following masses, measured to the nearest gram, using a suitable system of coding.

Mass (g)	241–244	245–248	249–252	253–256	257–260	261–264
Frequency	4	7	14	15	7	3

2 A production line produces steel bolts which have a nominal length of 95 mm. A sample of 50 bolts is taken and measured to the nearest 0.1 mm. Their deviations from 95 mm are recorded in tenths of a millimetre and summarised as $\sum x = -85$, $\sum x^2 = 734$. (For example, a bolt of length 94.2 mm would be recorded as -8.)

(i) Find the mean and standard deviation of the x values.

(ii) Find the mean and standard deviation of the lengths of the bolts in millimetres.

(iii) One of the figures recorded is -18. Suggest why this can be regarded as an outlier.

(iv) The figure of -18 is thought to be a mistake in the recording. Calculate the new mean and standard deviation of the lengths *in millimetres*, with the -18 value removed.

3 A survey of households in a particular area reveals that the mean and standard deviation of the number of units of electricity used in a quarter are 853 kW h and 279 kW h respectively. The cost per kW h is 7.2p and the standing charge is £12.56, excluding VAT.

  (i) Find the mean and standard deviation of the cost of the electricity used, excluding VAT.

  (ii) Find the mean and standard deviation of the cost of the electricity used, including VAT (at 17.5%).

4 A system is used in Avonford Technical College to predict a student's A level grade in a particular subject using their GCSE results. The GCSE score is g and the A level score is a and for Maths in 1999 the equation of the line of best fit relating them was $a = 2.6g - 9.42$.

This year there are 66 second-year students and their GCSE scores are summarised as $\sum g = 408.6$, $\sum g^2 = 2545.06$.

  (i) Find the mean and standard deviation of the GCSE scores.

  (ii) Find the mean and standard deviation of the predicted A level scores using the 1999 line of best fit.

5 (i) Find the mode, mean, mid-range and median of:

  2 8 6 5 4   5 6 3 6 4   9 1 5 6 5

  Hence write down, without further working, the mode, mean, mid-range and median of:

  (ii) 20 80 60 50 40   50 60 30 60 40   90 10 50 60 50
  (iii) 12 18 16 15 14   15 16 13 16 14   19 11 15 16 15
  (iv) 4 16 12 10 8   10 12 6 12 8   18 2 10 12 10

6 A manufacturer produces electrical cable which is sold on reels. The reels are supposed to hold 100 metres of cable. In the quality control department the length of cable on randomly chosen reels is measured. These measurements are recorded as deviations, in centimetres, from 100 m. (So, for example, a length of 99.84 m is recorded as -16.)

For a sample of 20 reels the recorded values, x, are summarised by

$$\sum x = -86 \qquad \sum x^2 = 4281$$

  (i) Calculate the mean and standard deviation of the values of x.
  (ii) Hence find the mean and standard deviation, in metres, of the lengths of cable on the 20 reels.
  (iii) Later it is noticed that one of the values of x is -47, and it is thought that so large a value is likely to be an error. Give a reason to support this view.
  (iv) Find the new mean and standard deviation of the values of x when the value -47 is discarded.

[MEI]

1 The following marks were obtained on an A Level mathematics paper by the candidates at one centre.

```
26 54 50   37 54      34 34 66 44 76      45 71   51 75 30
29 52 43   66 59      22 74 51 49 39      32 37   57 37 18
54 17 26   40 69      80 90 95 96 95      70 68   97 87 68
77 76 30 100 98       44 60 46 97 75      52 82   92 51 44
73 87 49   90 53      45 40 61 66 94      62 39 100 91 66
35 56 36   74 25      70 69 67 48 65      55 64
```

Draw a stem and leaf diagram to illustrate these marks and comment on their distribution.

2 The ages of a sample of 40 hang-gliders (in years) is given below.

```
28 19 24 20 28      26 22 19 37 40      19 25 65 34 66
35 69 65 26 17      22 26 45 58 30      31 58 26 29 23
72 23 21 30 28      65 21 67 23 57
```

(i) Using intervals of ten years, draw a stem and leaf diagram to illustrate these figures.

(ii) Comment on and give a possible explanation for the shape of the distribution.

3 An experimental fertiliser called GRO was applied to 50 lime trees, chosen at random, in a plantation. Another 50 trees were left untreated. The yields in kilograms were as follows:

Treated
```
59 25 52 19 32      26 33 24 35 30      23 54 33 31 25
23 61 35 38 44      27 24 30 62 23      47 42 41 53 31
20 21 41 33 35      38 61 63 44 18      53 38 33 49 54
50 44 25 42 18
```

Untreated
```
 8 11 22 22 20       5 31 40 14 45      10 16 14 20 51
55 30 30 25 29      12 48 17 12 52      58 61 14 32  5
29 40 61 53 22      33 41 62 51 56      10 48 50 14  8
63 43 61 12 42
```

Draw stem and leaf diagrams to compare the two sets of data and comment on the effects of GRO.

4 A group of 25 people were asked to estimate the length of a line which they were told was between 1 and 2 metres long. Here are their estimates, in metres.

> 1.15 1.33 1.42 1.26 1.29   1.30 1.30 1.46 1.18 1.24
> 1.21 1.30 1.32 1.33 1.29   1.30 1.40 1.26 1.32 1.30
> 1.41 1.28 1.65 1.54 1.14

(i) Represent these data in a sorted stem and leaf diagram.
(ii) From the stem and leaf diagram which you drew, read off the third highest and third lowest length estimates.
(iii) Find the middle of the 25 estimates.
(iv) On the evidence that you have, could you make an estimate of the length of the line? Justify your answer.

5 A recent survey of fee-paying schools found that one city had 11 such schools with the fee per pupil (correct to the nearest £100) being as follows.

> £3800   £11 100   £3500   £3700   £3800   £3100
> £2800   £3500   £3700   £3900   £3500

(i) Find the mean, median and mode of the data. Comment briefly on any substantial differences between these three measures.
(ii) Find the standard deviation of the data.
(iii) Explain whether the fee of £11 100 should be regarded as an outlier.

In fact the school charging £11 100 is a small school for musically talented pupils.

(iv) Explain why the mean as calculated in part (i) will **not** be the mean fee paid per pupil at the 11 schools.

[MEI]

6 On her summer holiday, Felicity recorded the temperatures at noon each day for use in a statistics project. The values recorded, f degrees Fahrenheit, were as follows, correct to the nearest degree.

> 47 59 68 62 49 67 66 73 70 68 74 84 80 72

(i) Represent Felicity's data on a stem and leaf diagram. (An unsorted diagram is sufficient.) Comment on the shape of the distribution.
(ii) Use your calculator to find the mean and standard deviation of Felicity's data.
(iii) The formula for converting temperatures from f degrees Fahrenheit to c degrees Celsius is $c = \frac{5}{9}(f - 32)$. *Use this formula* to estimate the mean and standard deviation of the temperatures in degrees Celsius.

[MEI]

7 In tenpin bowling the player attempts to knock down all ten skittles with one ball. If all ten are knocked down the player's turn ends without a second ball being bowled but if any skittles are left standing the player attempts to knock them down with a second ball. After the second ball the player's turn ends even if some skittles remain standing.

A novice player bowls a total of 34 balls. The numbers of skittles knocked down per ball are as follows.

Number of skittles	0	1	2	3	4	5	6	7	8	9	10
Frequency	6	3	1	7	8	3	2	3	0	1	0

(i) Use your calculator to determine the mean and standard deviation of the numbers of skittles knocked down per ball.

The diagrams below show, for two players A and B, the numbers of skittles knocked down per ball. (No scale is given on the frequency axis, but the data are for many hundreds of balls bowled.)

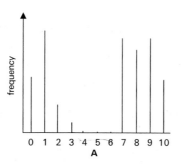 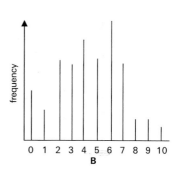

(ii) Without performing any calculations, **estimate** the mean number of skittles per ball knocked down by each of players A and B.

(iii) Without performing any calculations, compare the standard deviations for the two sets of data, explaining your reasoning.

(iv) One of the players is a considerably better bowler than the other. State which is which, giving your reasons carefully.

[MEI]

8 In the GCSE year of Old Hall High School there are 207 pupils. The school offers 16 subjects at GCSE. The numbers of pupils taking the various subjects are as follows.

Subject	A	B	C	D	E	F	G	H	I	J	K	L	M	N	O	P
Number	207	207	207	167	165	150	148	121	112	87	45	44	31	25	18	6

   (i) What do the data indicate about subjects A, B and C?
   (ii) Find the mean, median, mode and mid-range for the number of pupils per subject. Comment briefly on these as 'measures of central tendency'.
   (iii) Find the standard deviation of the number of pupils per subject.
   (iv) Determine the mean number of GCSEs taken per pupil.
   (v) Given that there are 79 different GCSE classes (with each pupil attending one class for each subject studied) determine the mean size of a GCSE class.

   [MEI]

9 A golf tournament is taking place. For each round, the players' scores are recorded relative to a fixed score of 72. (For example, a true score of 69 would be recorded as -3.)

   The recorded scores, x, for the ten players to complete the first round were:

$$4 \quad -3 \quad -7 \quad 6 \quad 2 \quad 0 \quad 0 \quad 3 \quad 5 \quad 2$$

   (i) Calculate the mean and standard deviation of the values of x.
   (ii) Deduce the mean and standard deviation of the true scores.

   In the second round of the tournament, the recorded scores, x, for the same ten golfers produced a mean of -0.3 and standard deviation 2.9.
   (iii) Comment on how the performance of the golfers has changed from the first to the second round.
   (iv) Calculate the mean and standard deviation of the twenty true scores for the two rounds.

   [MEI]

10 The hourly wages, £x, of the 15 workers in a small factory are as follows:

   £6.60   £3.40   £6.45   £5.20   £3.60   £7.25   £9.60   £3.75
   £4.20   £8.75   £5.75   £4.50   £3.95   £4.75   £12.25

   (i) Illustrate the data in a stem and leaf diagram, using pounds for the stem and pence for the leaves. Clearly indicate the median wage. State the range.
   (ii) Given that $\sum x = 90.00$ and $\sum x^2 = 631.25$, calculate the mean and standard deviation of hourly wages of the workers.

After delicate wage negotiations, the workers are offered a choice of one of the following pay rises:

(A) an increase of 30p per hour; (B) a 5% rise in hourly rates.

(iii) Use your answers in part (ii) to deduce the mean and standard deviation of the hourly wages of the 15 workers under both schemes.

(iv) Explain why the management would not mind which scheme was implemented, but the workers might.

[MEI]

11 A frequency diagram for a set of data is shown below. No scale is given on the frequency axis, but summary statistics are given for the distribution:

$$\sum f = 50, \qquad \sum fx = 100, \qquad \sum fx^2 = 344.$$

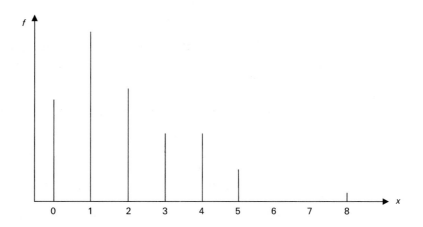

(i) State the mode and the mid-range value of the data.

(ii) Identify two features of the distribution.

(iii) Calculate the mean and standard deviation of the data and explain why the value 8, which occurs just once, may be regarded as an outlier.

(iv) Explain how you would treat the outlier if the diagram represents
   (a) the difference of the scores obtained when throwing a pair of ordinary dice
   (b) the number of children per household in a neighbourhood survey.

(v) Calculate new values for the mean and standard deviation if the single outlier is removed.

[MEI]

1 An item of data x may be identified as an *outlier* if $|x - \bar{x}| > 2 \times$ standard deviation. That is, if x is more than two standard deviations above or below the sample mean.

2 *Categorical data* are non-numerical; *discrete data* can be listed; *continuous data* can be measured to any degree of accuracy and it is not possible to list all values.

3 *Stem and leaf diagrams* (or stemplots) are suitable for discrete or continuous data. All data values are retained as well as indicating properties of the distribution.

4 The mean, median, mode or modal class and the mid-range are measures of central tendency.

5 The *mean*, $\bar{x} = \dfrac{\sum x}{n}$. For grouped data $\bar{x} = \dfrac{\sum xf}{n}$.

6 The *median* is the mid-value when the data are presented in rank order; it is

the value of the $\dfrac{n+1}{2}$ th item of n data items.

7 The *mode* is the most common item of data. The *modal class* is the class containing the most data, when the classes are of equal width.

8 The *mid-range* $= \frac{1}{2}$ (minimum data value + maximum data value)

9 The range, mean absolute deviation, the variance and the standard deviation are measures of *spread* or *dispersion*.

10 *Range* = maximum data value − minimum data value.

11 The *mean absolute deviation*, mad $= \dfrac{\sum |x - \bar{x}|}{n}$.

12 The variance $= \dfrac{1}{n} \sum (x - \bar{x})^2 f$ or $\dfrac{1}{n} \sum x^2 f - \bar{x}^2$.

13 The standard deviation $= \sqrt{\dfrac{1}{n} \sum (x - \bar{x})^2 f}$.

14 If data, represented by the variable x, are coded as $y = a + bx$ then the mean and standard deviation of the coded data are $\bar{y} = a + b\bar{x}$ and $sd_y = b \, sd_x$, respectively.

Data presentation and related measures of centre and spread

A picture is worth a thousand numbers.

Anon

THE AVONFORD STAR

Avonford top e-mail users league

Of a sample of 660 people surveyed in Avonford, 480 had their own e-mail address. They gained access to the Web via their own computers or through cable television. 95 people used their mobile phones to send and receive e-mails. 46 respondents sometimes used Avonford's Cyber Cafe. Samples were also taken in other towns of similar population size.

Of a sample of 720 people surveyed in Downlee only 29% had their own e-mail address.

Avonford residents' use of the Web varied from less than 1 hour per week to 12 hours per week. 50% of those who had their own e-mail address spent at least 8 hours on line each week compared to 20% of Downlee e-mailers.

Avonford's Mayor said today, 'This is very encouraging. I am optimistic that good use will be made of Avonford's own Web page.' Avonford's Web page can be found at www.avonford.town.ac.uk

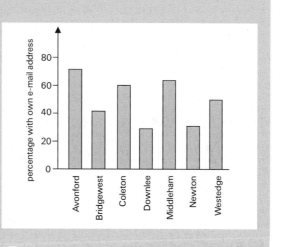

❓ How many Downlee residents have their own e-mail address?

How many Avonford residents use the Web for at least eight hours per week?

Some of the data the *Avonford Star* used in the article came from this table.

Town	Avonford	Bridgewest	Coleton	Downlee	Middleham	Newton	Westedge
Sample size	660	500	884	720	994	600	813
% with own e-mail	73	41	60	29	62	33	50

Most raw data need to be *summarised* to make it easier to see any patterns that may be present. You will often want to draw a diagram too. The *Avonford Star* used the table above to construct the the first diagram.

In Chapter 1 you saw some ways of illustrating data. For example, a frequency distribution table makes it immediately obvious where data are concentrated or if there are extreme values that need consideration. You also saw how data could be represented using a stem and leaf diagram. This method allows you to retain individual data values and at the same time present a picture of the distribution.

You will often want to use a diagram to communicate statistical findings. People find diagrams a very useful and easy way of presenting and understanding statistical information.

Bar charts and vertical line charts

It is best to use bar charts to illustrate categorical data and vertical line charts to illustrate discrete data, although people on occasion use them the other way round. The height of each bar or line represents the frequency.

 If bars are used there should be gaps between the bars. The widths and areas of the bars have no significance, but all the bars should be the same width to avoid distorting the picture of the data.

The political parties of the members of the Select Committee for Education and Employment, August 1999 (see page 12) are represented in the bar chart shown in figure 2.1. It is immediately obvious that the Labour party has a majority membership of this committee.

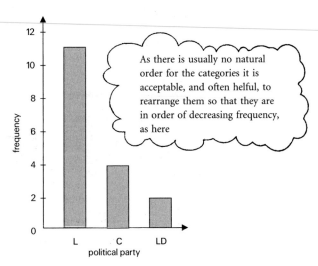

As there is usually no natural order for the categories it is acceptable, and often helful, to rearrange them so that they are in order of decreasing frequency, as here

Figure 2.1 *A bar chart illustrating categorical data*

Rachel plays cricket for the Avonford Amazons Cricket Club. During her first season, in which she batted and bowled for the team, she summarised her batting record in the following diagram.

Even though a bar chart can be used in this example, a line chart is preferable as it shows quite clearly that the scores can only take integer values.

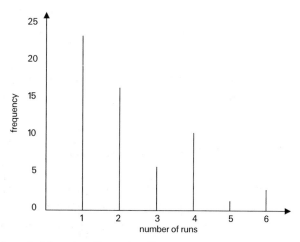

Figure 2.2 *A vertical line chart illustrating discrete data*

There are many different ways of drawing bar charts. The bars can be horizontal or vertical. The bars can also be subdivided. A compound bar chart is shown in figure 2.3. Often there is no single right way of displaying the information; what is most important is that it should be easy to follow and not misleading.

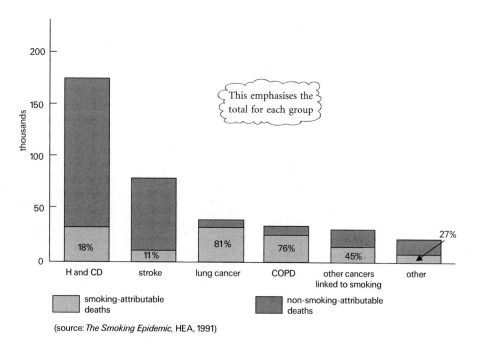

(source: *The Smoking Epidemic*, HEA, 1991)

Figure 2.3 *Compound bar chart showing smoking- and non-smoking-attributable deaths*

Figure 2.4 shows a multiple bar chart comparing the level of sales of three products of a company over a period of four years. Note that there is a gap between the information for each year.

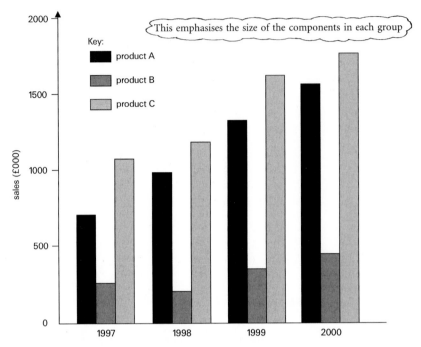

Figure 2.4

Pie charts

A pie chart can be used to illustrate categorical (or qualitative) data or it can be used to illustrate discrete or grouped continuous data. Pie charts are used to show the size of constituent parts relative to the whole.

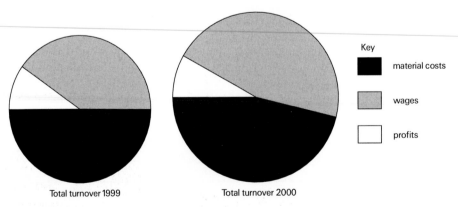

Figure 2.5

Avonford Electronics increased their turnover from £1 800 000 in 1999 to £2 400 000 in 2000. The pie charts show the division of the money between wages, material costs and profits.

The increase in total turnover from 1999 to 2000 is reflected in the larger area of the second pie chart.

The values of the data are proportional to the areas of the pie charts and not proportional to the radii.

For example: Area of chart 2 $= \frac{4}{3} \times$ area of chart 1

? Measure the radii of the pie charts. Are they consistent with the data?

How can you see from these pie charts that proportionally more is spent on wages in 2000 than in 1999?

Has the actual amount spent on wages increased?

Some statisticians feel that in most cases a bar chart is a better choice. Why do you think this is?

EXERCISE 2A

1 (a) State whether the data described below are categorical or numerical, and, if numerical, whether discrete or continuous.

(b) State what you think would be the most appropriate method of displaying the data.

(i) The number of coins in shoppers' purses

(ii) The colour of the eyes of a sample of people

(iii) The masses of a sample of eggs

(iv) The medals (gold, silver and bronze) won by a team at the Olympic games

(v) The sizes of a sample of eggs (size 1, size 2, etc.)

(vi) The times of the runners in a 100-metre race

(vii) The numbers on the shirts of a sample of rugby players

(viii) The scores of the competitors in an ice-skating competition

(ix) Estimates of the length of a needle

(x) The single letter on the registration plate of a sample of cars.

2 The two pie charts are drawn to scale. They represent the income of two North Atlantic islands one year. The total income for Seanna was £72 000. Calculate the earnings for both islands from each product.

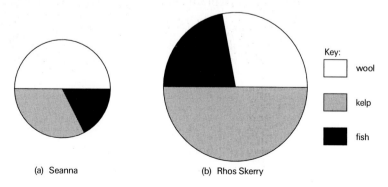

(a) Seanna   (b) Rhos Skerry

Key:
wool
kelp
fish

3 A developing country's education budget is divided between the the primary, secondary and tertiary sectors. The figures below give the amount of money spent on each sector. They are in millions of dollars and have been adjusted to allow for inflation.

	Primary	Secondary	Tertiary
1960	4.1	1.1	0.9
1975	12.2	8.4	6.0
1990	18.0	20.8	16.9

(i) Draw compound bar charts to illustrate this information.

(ii) Draw, to scale, three pie charts to illustrate the information.

(iii) Comment briefly on what the figures tell you about the country's education programme.

(iv) Which do you consider to be the better method of display and why?

4 The compound bar chart shows the production of three cash crops from a region of an African country in the years 1990 and 2000.

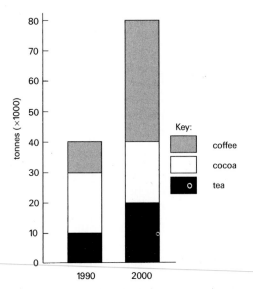

(i) Draw, to scale, two pie charts to illustrate the same information.

(ii) Comment on the changes in crop production over the ten years.

(iii) Which do you consider to be the better method of display and why?

5 The following table shows the breakdown of information for *Workright Co. Ltd* over a four-year period.

	1997 (£m)	1998 (£m)	1999 (£m)	2000 (£m)
Turnover	4.0	4.5	5.8	6.0
Wages	1.3	1.9	2.2	2.5
Production costs	0.4	0.5	0.6	0.8
Material costs	1.0	1.3	1.6	1.8
Taxation	0.2	0.1	0.3	0.0
Other costs	0.5	0.5	0.7	0.8
Profit	0.6	0.2	0.4	0.1

(i) Illustrate the above data using an appropriate diagram.

(ii) Comment on the company's performance.

6 Data for *Avonford Electronics* for 1999 and 2000 are shown in the table below.

	Turnover	Material costs	Wages	Profits
1999	£1 800 000	£900 000	£720 000	£180 000
2000	£2 400 000	£1 100 000	£1 100 000	£200 000

Draw an appropriate bar chart to compare the data for 1999 and 2000.

Histograms

Histograms are used to illustrate continuous data. The columns in a histogram may have different widths and it is the area of each column which is proportional to the frequency and not the height. Unlike bar charts, there are no gaps between the columns because where one class ends the next begins.

Continuous data with equal class widths

A sample of 60 components is taken from a production line and their diameters, d mm, recorded. The resulting data are summarised in the following frequency table.

Length (mm)	Frequency
$25 \leqslant d < 30$	1
$30 \leqslant d < 35$	3
$35 \leqslant d < 40$	7
$40 \leqslant d < 45$	15
$45 \leqslant d < 50$	17
$50 \leqslant d < 55$	10
$55 \leqslant d < 60$	5
$60 \leqslant d < 65$	2

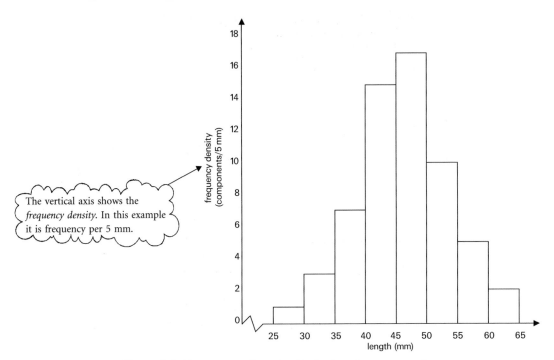

The vertical axis shows the *frequency density*. In this example it is frequency per 5 mm.

Figure 2.6 *Histogram to show the distribution of component diameters*

The class boundaries are 25, 30, 35, 40, 45, 50, 55, 60 and 65. The width of each class is 5.

The area of each column is proportional to the class frequency. In this example the class widths are equal so the height of each column is also proportional to the class frequency.

The column representing $45 \leqslant d < 50$ is the highest and this tells you that this is the modal class, that is, the class with highest frequency per 5 mm.

? How would you identify the modal class if the intervals were not of equal width?

Labelling the frequency axis

The vertical axis tells you the frequency *density*. Figure 2.8 looks the same as 2.7 but it is not a histogram. This type of diagram is, however, often incorrectly referred to as a histogram. It is more correctly called a frequency chart. A histogram shows the frequency density on the vertical axis.

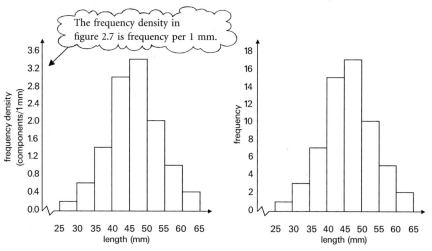

Figure 2.7   **Figure 2.8**

The units which you choose for the frequency density are particularly important when the class widths are unequal, as you will see in the next example.

Continuous data with unequal class widths

The heights of 80 broad bean plants were measured, correct to the nearest centimetre, ten weeks after planting. The data are summarised in the frequency table.

Height (cm)	Frequency	Class width (cm)	Frequency per 2 cm
$7.5 \leqslant x < 11.5$	1	4	$\frac{1}{2}$
$11.5 \leqslant x < 13.5$	3	2	3
$13.5 \leqslant x < 15.5$	7	2	7
$15.5 \leqslant x < 17.5$	11	2	11
$17.5 \leqslant x < 19.5$	19	2	19
$19.5 \leqslant x < 21.5$	14	2	14
$21.5 \leqslant x < 23.5$	13	2	13
$23.5 \leqslant x < 25.5$	9	2	9
$25.5 \leqslant x < 28.5$	3	3	2

Most of the classes are 2 cm wide so it is convenient to take 2 cm as the *standard width*.

The first class is twice the standard width; consequently the height of this column on the histogram is half the given frequency. The last class is $\frac{3}{2}$ times the standard width so the height of the column is $\frac{2}{3}$ of the given frequency. The area of each column is proportional to the class frequency.

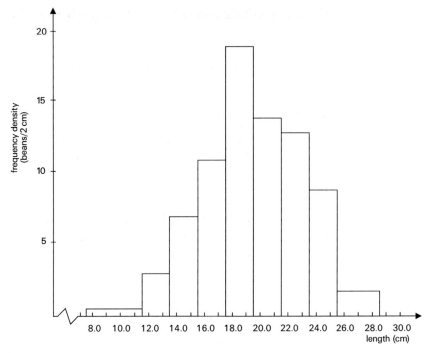

Figure 2.9

Discrete data

 Histograms are occasionally used for grouped *discrete* data. However, you should always first consider the alternatives.

A test was given to 100 students. The maximum mark was 70. The raw data are shown below.

10	18	68	67	25	62	49	11	12	8
9	46	53	57	30	63	34	21	68	31
20	16	29	13	31	56	9	34	45	55
35	40	45	48	54	50	34	32	47	60
70	52	21	25	53	41	29	63	43	50
40	48	45	38	51	25	52	55	47	46
46	50	8	25	56	18	20	36	36	9
38	39	53	45	42	42	61	55	30	38
62	47	58	54	59	25	24	53	42	61
18	30	32	45	49	28	31	27	54	38

Illustrating this data using a vertical line graph results in the following:

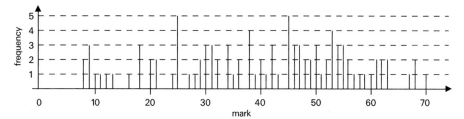

Figure 2.10

This diagram fails to give a clear picture of the overall distribution of marks. In this case you could consider a bar chart or, as the individual marks are known, a stem and leaf diagram, as follows.

$n = 100$

2 | 5   represents 25 marks

```
0 | 8 8 9 9 9
1 | 0 1 2 3 6 8 8 8
2 | 0 0 1 1 4 5 5 5 5 5 7 8 9 9
3 | 0 0 0 1 1 1 2 2 4 4 4 5 6 6 8 8 8 8 9
4 | 0 0 1 2 2 2 3 5 5 5 5 5 6 6 6 7 7 7 8 8 9 9
5 | 0 0 0 1 2 2 3 3 3 3 4 4 4 5 5 5 6 6 7 8 9
6 | 0 1 1 2 2 3 3 7 8 8
7 | 0
```

Figure 2.11

If the data have been grouped and the original data have been lost, or are otherwise unknown, then a histogram may be considered. A grouped frequency table and histogram illustrating the marks are shown below.

Marks, x	Frequency, f
0–9	5
10–19	8
20–29	14
30–39	19
40–49	22
50–59	21
60–70	11

Data presentation and related measures of centre and spread

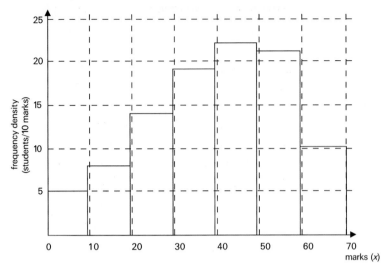

Figure 2.12

Note

The class boundary 10–19 becomes $9.5 \leqslant x < 19.5$ for the purpose of drawing the histogram. You must give careful consideration to class boundaries, particularly if you are using rounded data.

? Look at the intervals for the first and last classes. How do they differ from the others? Why is this the case?

Grouped discrete data are illustrated well by a histogram if the distribution is particularly skewed as is the case in the next example.

The first 50 positive integers squared are:

1	4	9	16	25	36	49	64
81	100	121	144	169	196	225	256
289	324	361	400	441	484	529	576
625	676	729	784	841	900	961	1024
1089	1156	1225	1296	1369	1444	1521	1600
1681	1764	1849	1936	2025	2116	2209	2304
2401	2500						

Number, n	Frequency, f
$0 < n \leqslant 250$	15
$250 < n \leqslant 500$	7
$500 < n \leqslant 750$	5
$750 < n \leqslant 1000$	4
$1000 < n \leqslant 1250$	4
$1250 < n \leqslant 1500$	3
$1500 < n \leqslant 1750$	3
$1750 < n \leqslant 2000$	3
$2000 < n \leqslant 2250$	3
$2250 < n \leqslant 2500$	3

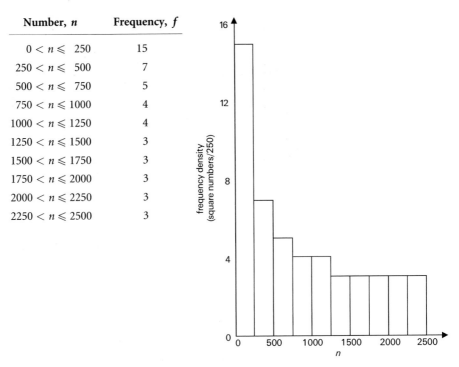

Figure 2.13

The main points to remember when drawing a histogram are:

- Histograms are usually used for illustrating continuous data. For discrete data it is better to draw a stem and leaf diagram, line graph or bar chart.
- Since the data are continuous, or treated as if they were continuous, adjacent columns of the histogram should touch (unlike a bar chart where the columns should be drawn with gaps between them).
- It is the areas and not the heights of the columns that are proportional to the frequency of each class.
- The vertical axis should be marked with the appropriate frequency density (*frequency per 5 mm* for example), rather than frequency.

EXERCISE 2B

1 A number of trees in two woods were measured. Their diameters, correct to the nearest centimetre, are summarised in the table below.

Diameter (cm)	1–10	11–15	16–20	21–30	31–50	Total
Akeley Wood	10	5	3	11	1	30
Shaw's Wood	6	8	20	5	1	40

(Trees less than $\frac{1}{2}$ cm in diameter are not included.)

(i) Write down the actual class boundaries.

(ii) Draw two separate histograms to illustrate this information.

(iii) State the modal class for each wood.

(iv) Describe the main features of the distributions for the two woods.

2 Listed below are the prime numbers, p, from 1 up to 1000. (1 itself is not usually defined as a prime.)

Primes up to 1000

2	3	5	7	11	13	17	19	23	29	31	37	41	43
47	53	59	61	67	71	73	79	83	89	97	101	103	107
109	113	127	131	137	139	149	151	157	163	167	173	179	181
191	193	197	199	211	223	227	229	233	239	241	251	257	263
269	271	277	281	283	293	307	311	313	317	331	337	347	349
353	359	367	373	379	383	389	397	401	409	419	421	431	433
439	443	449	457	461	463	467	479	487	491	499	503	509	521
523	541	547	557	563	569	571	577	587	593	599	601	607	613
617	619	631	641	643	647	653	659	661	673	677	683	691	701
709	719	727	733	739	743	751	757	761	769	773	787	797	809
811	821	823	827	829	839	853	857	859	863	877	881	883	887
907	911	919	929	937	941	947	953	967	971	977	983	991	997

(i) Draw a histogram to illustrate these data with the following class intervals:
$1 \leqslant p < 20 \quad 20 \leqslant p < 50 \quad 50 \leqslant p < 100 \quad 100 \leqslant p < 200$
$200 \leqslant p < 300 \quad 300 \leqslant p < 500$ and $500 \leqslant p < 1000$.

(ii) Comment on the shape of the distribution.

3 A case containing 270 oranges was opened and each orange was weighed to the nearest gram. The masses were found to be distributed as in the following table:

Mass (grams)	Number of oranges
60–99	20
100–119	60
120–139	80
140–159	50
160–219	60

(i) Draw a histogram to illustrate the data.

(ii) From the table, calculate an estimate of the mean mass of an orange from this crate.

4 In an agricultural experiment, 320 plants were grown on a plot, and the lengths of the stems were measured to the nearest centimetre ten weeks after planting. The lengths were found to be distributed as in the following table:

Length (cm)	Number of plants
20–31	30
32–37	80
38–43	90
44–49	60
50–67	60

(i) Draw a histogram to illustrate the data.

(ii) From the table, calculate an estimate of the mean length of stem of a plant from this experiment.

5 The lengths of time of sixty songs recorded by a certain group of singers are summarised in the table below:

Song length in seconds (x)	Number of songs
$0 < x < 120$	1
$120 \leqslant x < 180$	9
$180 \leqslant x < 240$	15
$240 \leqslant x < 300$	17
$300 \leqslant x < 360$	13
$360 \leqslant x \leqslant 600$	5

(i) Display the data on a histogram.

(ii) Determine the mean song length.

Measures of central tendency and of spread using quartiles

You saw in Chapter 1 how to find the median of a set of discrete data. As a reminder, the median is the value of the middle item when all the data items have been ranked in order.

The median is the value of the $\frac{n+1}{2}$th item and is half-way through the data set. The values one-quarter of the way through the data set and three-quarters of the way through the data set are called the *lower quartile* and the *upper quartile* respectively. The lower quartile, median and upper quartile are usually denoted using Q_1, Q_2 and Q_3.

Quartiles are used mainly with large data sets and their values found by looking at the $\frac{1}{4}$, $\frac{1}{2}$ and $\frac{3}{4}$ points. So, for a data set of 1000, you would take Q_1 to be the value of the 250th data item, Q_2 to be the value of the 500th data item and Q_3 to be the value of the 750th data item.

 It's better to avoid using quartiles with small data sets or samples since the value of any of them is heavily dependent on one or two members of the set. If you cannot avoid working with a small sample then the median is the value of the $\frac{n+1}{2}$th item. If $\frac{n+1}{2}$ is a whole number value, m, you use $\frac{m+1}{2}$ to find the position of the lower quartile. So, for a data set of nine items Q_2 is the value of the fifth item ($\frac{9+1}{2}$). Q_1 is the value of the third item ($\frac{5+1}{2}$) from the bottom of the data set and Q_3 is the value of the third item from the top of the data set. If $\frac{n+1}{2}$ is a half value, ignore the half to find Q_1 and Q_3, as shown in the example.

EXAMPLE 2.1

Catherine is a junior reporter at the *Avonford Star*. As part of an investigation into consumer affairs she purchases 0.5 kg of lean mince from 12 shops and supermarkets in the town. The resulting data, put into rank order, are as follows:

£1.39 £1.39 £1.46 £1.48 £1.48 £1.50 £1.52 £1.54 £1.60 £1.65 £1.68 £1.72

Find Q_1, Q_2 and Q_3.

SOLUTION

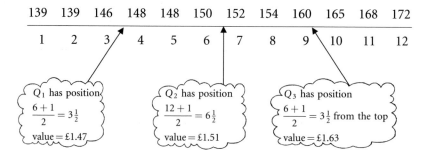

In fact, the upper quartile has a value of £1.625 but this has been rounded up to the nearest penny.

⚠ You may encounter different formulae for finding the lower and upper quartiles. The ones given here are relatively easy to calculate and usually lead to values of Q_1 and Q_3 which are close to the true values.

❓ What are the true values?

Interquartile range or quartile spread

The difference between the lower and upper quartiles is known as the *interquartile range* or *quartile spread*.

Interquartile range $(IQR) = Q_3 - Q_1.$

In Example 2.1 $IQR = 163 - 147 = 16$p.

The interquartile range covers the middle 50% of the data. It is relatively easy to calculate and is a useful measure of spread as it avoids extreme values. It is said to be resistant to outliers.

Box and whisker plots (boxplots)

The three quartiles and the two extreme values of a data set may be illustrated in a *box and whisker plot*. This is designed to give an easy-to-read representation of the location and spread of a distribution. Figure 2.14 shows a box and whisker plot for the data in Example 2.1.

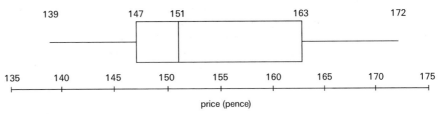

Figure 2.14

The box represents the middle 50% of the distribution and the whiskers stretch out to the extreme values.

Figure 2.15 shows a box and whisker plot for the data relating to the ages of the cyclists involved in accidents in Avonford discussed in Chapter 1.

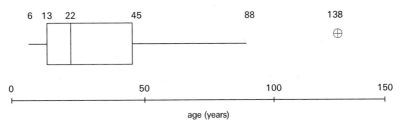

Figure 2.15

From the diagram you can see that the distribution has positive or right skewness. The ⊕ indicates an outlier and is above the upper quartile. Outliers are usually labelled as they are often of special interest. The whiskers are drawn to the most extreme data points which are not outliers.

Outliers

Data which are at least $1.5 \times IQR$ beyond the upper or lower quartile are outliers. Extreme outliers are at least $3 \times IQR$ beyond the upper or lower quartile.

Cumulative frequency curves

When working with large data sets or grouped data, percentiles and quartiles can be found from *cumulative frequency curves* as shown in the next section.

THE AVONFORD STAR

Letters to the editor

Dear sir,
I am a student trying to live on a government loan. I'm trying my best to allow myself a sensible monthly budget but my lecturers have given me a long list of textbooks to buy. If I buy just half of them I will have nothing left to live on this month. The majority of books on my list are over £16.

I want to do well at my studies but I won't do well without books and I won't do well if I am ill through not eating properly.

Please tell me what to do, and don't say 'go to the library' because the books I need are never there.

Yours faithfully,
Sheuli Roberts

After receiving this letter the editor wondered if there was a story in it. She asked a reporter to carry out a survey of the prices of textbooks in a large shop. The reporter took a large sample of 470 textbooks and the results are summarised in the table.

Cost, C (£)	Frequency (No. of books)
$C < 10$	13
$10 \leqslant C < 15$	53
$15 \leqslant C < 20$	97
$20 \leqslant C < 25$	145
$25 \leqslant C < 30$	81
$30 \leqslant C < 35$	40
$35 \leqslant C < 40$	23
$40 \leqslant C < 45$	12
$45 \leqslant C < 50$	6

He decided to estimate the median and the upper and lower quartiles of the costs of the books. (Without the original data you cannot find the actual values so all calculations will be estimates.) The first step is to make a cumulative frequency table, then to plot a cumulative frequency curve.

Cost, C (£)	Frequency	Cost	Cumulative frequency	
$0 \leqslant C < 10$	13	$C < 10$	13	
$10 \leqslant C < 15$	53	$C < 15$	66◄	See Note 1
$15 \leqslant C < 20$	97	$C < 20$	163◄	See Note 2
$20 \leqslant C < 25$	145	$C < 25$	308	
$25 \leqslant C < 30$	81	$C < 30$	389	
$30 \leqslant C < 35$	40	$C < 35$	429	
$35 \leqslant C < 40$	23	$C < 40$	452	
$40 \leqslant C < 45$	12	$C < 45$	464	
$45 \leqslant C < 50$	6	$C < 50$	470	

Notes

1 Notice that the interval $C < 15$ means $0 \leqslant C < 15$ and so includes the 13 books in the interval $0 \leqslant C < 10$ and the 53 books in the interval $10 \leqslant C < 15$, giving 66 books in total.

2 Similarly, to find the total for the interval $C < 20$ you must add the number of books in the interval $15 \leqslant C < 20$ to your previous total, giving you $66 + 97 = 163$.

A cumulative frequency curve is obtained by plotting the *upper boundary* of each class against the cumulative frequency. The points are joined by a smooth curve, as shown in figure 2.16.

In this example the actual values are unknown and the median must therefore be an estimate. It is usual in such cases to find the *estimated* value of the $\frac{n}{2}$th item. This gives a better estimate of the median than is obtained by using $\frac{n+1}{2}$, which is used for ungrouped data. Similarly, estimates of the lower and upper quartiles are found from the $\frac{n}{4}$th and $\frac{3n}{4}$th items.

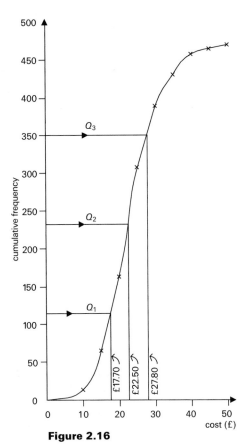

Figure 2.16

The 235th $\left(\frac{470}{2}\right)$ item of data identifies the median which has a value of about £22.50. The 117.5th $\left(\frac{470}{4}\right)$ item of data identifies the lower quartile, which has a value of about £17.70 and the 352.5th $\left(\frac{3}{4} \times 470\right)$ item of data identifies the upper quartile, which has a value of about £27.70.

Notice the distinctive shape of the cumulative frequency curve. It is like a stretched out S-shape leaning forwards.

What about Sheuli's claim that the majority of textbooks cost more than £16? $Q_1 = £17.70$. By definition 75% of books are more expensive than this, so Sheuli's claim seems to be well founded. We need to check exactly how many books are estimated to be more expensive than £16.

From the cumulative frequency curve 85 books cost £16 or less. So 385 books or about 82% are more expensive.

 You should be cautious about any conclusions you draw. This example deals with books many of which have prices like £9.95 or £39.99. In using a cumulative frequency curve you are assuming an even spread of data throughout the intervals and this may not always be the case.

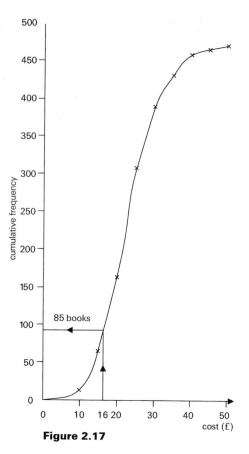

Figure 2.17

Box and whisker plots for grouped data

It is often helpful to draw a box and whisker plot. In cases such as the above when the extreme values are unknown the whiskers are drawn out to the 10th and 90th percentiles. Arrows indicate that the minimum and maximum values are further out.

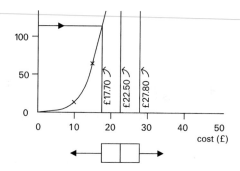

Figure 2.18

1 For each of the following sets of figures, find

  (a) the range

  (b) the median

  (c) the upper and lower quartiles

  (d) the interquartile range.

  (i)   6 8 3 2 1   5 4 6 8 5   6 7 8 8 6 6

  (ii)   12 5 17 11 4   10 12 19 12 5   9 15 11 16 8

          18 12 8 9 11   12 14 8 14 7

  (iii) 25 28 29 30 20   23 23 27 25 28

  (iv)   115 123 132 109 127   116 128 132 114 109

          125 134 121 117 118   117 116 123 105 125

  (v)   2 8 4 6 3   5 1 8 2 5   8 0 3 7 8 5

  (vi)   12 18 14 16 13   15 11 18 12 15   18 10 13 17 18 15

  (vii) 272 278 274 276 273   275 271 278 272 275   278 270 273 277 278 275

  (viii) 20 80 40 60 30   50 10 80 20 50   80 0 30 70 80 50

2 Find

  (i)   the median

  (ii)   the upper and lower quartiles

  (iii) the interquartile range

  for the scores of golfers in the first round of a competition.

  70 |

  71 ||

  72 ||||

  73   ⊔⊔⊤ |||

  74   ⊔⊔⊤ ⊔⊔⊤ ||

  75   ⊔⊔⊤ ||

  76   ⊔⊔⊤

  77   ⊔⊔⊤ |

  78

  79 |||

  80 |

  81

  82 |

  (iv) Illustrate the data with a box and whisker plot.

  (v) The scores for the second round are illustrated on the box and whisker plot below. Compare the two and say why you think the differences might have arisen.

   67   68   70   74   77

3 The number of goals scored by a hockey team in its matches one season are illustrated on the vertical line chart below.

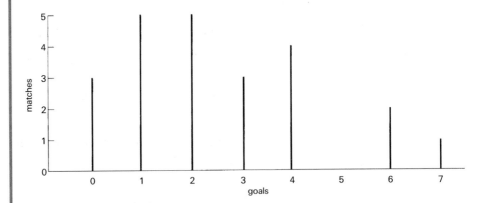

(i) Draw a box and whisker plot to illustrate the same data.

(ii) State, with reasons, which you think is the better method of display in this case.

4 One year the yields, y, of a number of walnut trees were recorded to the nearest kilogram as follows:

Yield, y (kg)	Frequency
40–49	1
50–59	5
60–69	7
70–79	4
80–89	2
90–99	1

(i) Construct the cumulative frequency table for these data.

(ii) Draw the cumulative frequency graph.

(iii) Use your graph to estimate the median and interquartile range of the yields.

(iv) Draw a box and whisker plot to illustrate the data.

The piece of paper where the actual figures had been recorded was then found, and these were:

> 44 59 67 76 52   62 68 78 53 63   69 82 53 65 70
> 85 93 56 65 74

(v) Use these data to find the median and interquartile range and compare your answers with those you obtained from the grouped data.

(vi) What are the advantages and disadvantages of grouping data?

1   The status of the 120 full-time employees of a small factory is linked to their pay.

Status	Pay (£P/week)
Unskilled	$120 \leqslant P < 200$
Skilled	$200 \leqslant P < 280$
Staff	$280 \leqslant P < 400$
Management	$400 \leqslant P < 1000$

The company's personnel department illustrate the numbers in the various groups on this accurately drawn pie chart.

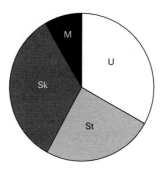

(i)   Copy and complete this table, finding the frequencies from the pie chart.

Status	Interval (pay £P/week)	Frequency (employees)	Interval length (×£10)	Frequency density (employees/£10)
Unskilled	$120 \leqslant P < 200$	40	8	5.0
Skilled	$200 \leqslant P < 280$			
Staff	$280 \leqslant P < 400$			
Management	$400 \leqslant P < 1000$			

(ii)   Hence draw a histogram to illustrate the data.

(iii)   Is the shape of the histogram about what you would expect?

(iv)   State, with reasons, which you think is the more appropriate method of display.

2

UK motorcycle casualties, by age, 1989

Age (years)	Casualties (%)
16–19	36
20–24	26
25–29	15
30–39	11
40–80	12

(Source *Social Trends* 21)

(i) Draw a pie chart to illustrate the data, using the five groups given.

(ii) Write down the ages of the youngest and oldest person who would come within the interval written as 16–19.

(iii) Draw a histogram to represent the data.

(iv) Comment on the information in the table, stating with reasons what you consider to be the most and the least dangerous ages for motorcyclists. Do you have enough information to answer this as fully as you would wish?

(v) State, with reasons, which you find the more helpful method of display, the pie chart or the histogram.

3 After completing a long assignment, a student was told by his tutor that it was more like a book than an essay. He decided to investigate how many pages there are in a typical book and started by writing down the numbers of pages in the books on one of his shelves, as follows:

$$
\begin{array}{llllllllll}
256 & 128 & 160 & 128 & 192 & 64 & 356 & 96 & 64 & 160 \\
464 & 128 & 96 & 96 & 556 & 148 & 64 & 192 & 96 & 512 \\
940 & 676 & 128 & 196 & 640 & 44 & 64 & 144 & 256 & 72
\end{array}
$$

(i) Look carefully at the data and state, giving your reasons, whether they are continuous or discrete. Give an explanation for your answer.

(ii) Decide on the most helpful method of displaying the data and draw the appropriate diagram.

4 The intervals of time between successive emissions from a weak radioactive source were measured for 200 consecutive intervals, with the following results:

Interval (seconds)	0–5	6–10	11–15	16–20	21–25	26–30	31–35
Frequency	23	67	42	26	21	15	6

(i) Draw a cumulative frequency graph for this distribution.

(ii) Use your graph to estimate
   (a) the median
   (b) the interquartile range.

(iii) Calculate an estimate of the mean of the distribution.

[MEI]

5 In a sample of 800 eggs from an egg farm each egg was weighed and classified according to its mass to the nearest gram. The frequency distribution was as follows:

Mass in grams	41–45	46–50	51–55	56–60	61–65	66–70
Number of eggs	36	142	286	238	76	22

Draw a cumulative frequency graph of the data, using a scale of 2 cm to represent 5 grams on the horizontal axis (which should be labelled from 40 to 70 grams) and a scale of 2 cm to represent 100 eggs on the vertical axis.

Use your graph to estimate for this sample
(i) the percentage of eggs which would be classified as large (over 62 grams)
(ii) the median mass of an egg
(iii) the interquartile range.
Indicate clearly on your diagram how you arrive at your results.

6 The following table gives the age distribution of 3137 holders of a specific type of life assurance policy.

Age	Frequency	Age	Frequency
21–25	44	61–65	396
26–30	47	66–70	488
31–35	66	71–75	471
36–40	107	76–80	358
41–45	147	81–85	222
46–50	151	86–90	104
51–55	208	91–95	18
56–60	305	96–100	5

(i) Estimate the mean age of a policyholder.
(ii) Calculate also the median age and the upper and lower quartiles.
(iii) Plot the data on a cumulative frequency graph and from this estimate the median age and the upper and lower quartiles. Compare these values with the values previously calculated.

[MEI (adapted)]

7 At a plant breeding institute, two different strains of a certain species of plant were compared by measuring the length, to the nearest millimetre, of each of 100 leaves of each strain. The results recorded are shown in the table.

Length of leaf (mm)	Frequency		Length of leaf (mm)	Frequency	
	Strain A	Strain B		Strain A	Strain B
Under 10	3	1	30–34	11	25
10–14	6	4	35–39	6	20
15–19	11	6	40–44	4	11
20–24	22	10	45–49	1	4
25–29	35	16	Over 50	1	3

(i) Draw up a cumulative frequency table for each set of results. On the same axes draw the corresponding cumulative frequency graphs. (Scales: 2 cm ≡ 10 mm horizontally, 2 cm ≡ 10 leaves vertically.)

(ii) Use your graphs to deduce which strain should be developed

    (a) to produce plants with longer leaves

    (b) to produce plants with uniformity of length of leaf.

    Give numerical readings taken from your graphs to support your conclusions.

[MEI (part)]

8 *Gross weekly earnings of adults in full-time employment, April 1990 (£)*

	Manual		Non-manual	
	Men	Women	Men	Women
Upper quartile	280	171	414	264
Median	221	137	312	191
Lower quartile	174	112	231	147

(Source: New Earnings Survey, 1990)

(i) Look at these figures and state what you conclude from them.

(ii) Using the interquartile range as the measure, compare the spread of the earnings of women with that of men, both manual and non-manual.

9 The table summarises the observed lifetimes, x, in seconds, of 50 fruit flies subjected to a new spray in a controlled experiment.

Interval	Mid-interval value	Frequency
$0.5 \leqslant x < 5.5$	3	3
$5.5 \leqslant x < 10.5$	8	22
$10.5 \leqslant x < 15.5$	13	12
$15.5 \leqslant x < 20.5$	18	9
$20.5 \leqslant x < 25.5$	23	2
$25.5 \leqslant x < 30.5$	28	1
$30.5 \leqslant x < 35.5$	33	1

(i) Making clear your methods and showing all your working, estimate the mean and standard deviation of these lifetimes. Give your answers correct to 3 significant figures and do not make any corrections for grouping.

(ii) Draw the cumulative frequency graph and use it to estimate the minimum lifetime below which 70% of all lifetimes lie.

10 A random sample of 200 batteries, of nominal potential 6 V, was taken from a very large batch of batteries. The potential difference between the terminals of each battery was measured, resulting in the table of data opposite:

Calculate the mean and standard deviation of these voltages and illustrate the data on a histogram. Mark clearly on the histogram the mean voltage and the voltages which are two standard deviations either side of the mean.

[MEI]

Potential difference in volts (mid-interval value)	Number of batteries
5.80	1
5.85	4
5.90	22
5.95	42
6.00	60
6.05	44
6.10	24
6.15	2
6.20	1

KEY POINTS

1 Bar charts:
   - commonly used to illustrate categorical data
   - vertical axis labelled *frequency*
   - bars usually not touching.

2 Vertical line graphs:
   - commonly used to illustrate discrete data
   - vertical axis labelled *frequency*.

3 Pie charts:
   - total frequency is proportional to area.

4 Histograms:
   - commonly used to illustrate continuous data
   - horizontal axis shows the variable being measured (cm, kg, etc.)
   - vertical axis labelled with the appropriate *frequency density* (per 10 cm, per 100 kg, etc.)
   - no gaps between columns
   - the *frequency density* is *proportional* to the *area* of each column.

5 For a small data set with n items of data,
   - the median, Q_2, is the value of the $\frac{n+1}{2}$th item of data.
   If $\frac{n+1}{2}$ is a whole number, m,
   - the lower quartile, Q_1, is the value of the $\frac{m+1}{2}$th item of data
   - the upper quartile, Q_3, is the value of the $m + \frac{m+1}{2}$th item of data.
   If m is not a whole number ignore the fraction part.

6 Interquartile range $(IQR) = Q_3 - Q_1$.

7 When data are illustrated using a cumulative frequency curve the median, lower and upper quartiles are estimated by identifying the data values with cumulative frequencies $\frac{n}{2}$, $\frac{n}{4}$ and $\frac{3n}{4}$.

8 A box and whisker plot is a useful way of summarising data and showing the median, upper and lower quartiles and any outliers.

3 Probability

If we knew Lady Luck better, Las Vegas would still be a roadstop in the desert.

Stephen Jay Gould

A library without books

If you plan to pop into the Avonford library and pick up the latest bestseller, then forget it. All the best books 'disappear' practically as soon as they are put on the shelves.

I talked about the problem with the local senior librarian, Gina Clarke.

'We have a real problem with unauthorised loans at the moment,' Gina told me. 'Out of our total stock of, say, 80 000 books, something like 44 000 are out on loan at any one time. About 20 000 are on the shelves and I'm afraid the rest are unaccounted for.'

That means that the probability of finding the particular book you want is exactly $\frac{1}{4}$. With odds like that, don't bet on being lucky next time you visit your library.

Librarian Gina Clarke is worried about the problem of 'disappearing books'

How do you think the figure of $\frac{1}{4}$ at the end of the article was arrived at? Do you agree that the probability is *exactly* $\frac{1}{4}$?

The information about the different categories of book can be summarised as follows.

Category of book	Typical numbers
On the shelves	20 000
Out on loan	44 000
Unauthorised loan	16 000
Total stock	80 000

On the basis of these figures it is possible to estimate the probability of finding the book you want. Of the total stock of 80 000 books bought by the library, you might expect to find about 20 000 on the shelves at any one time. As a fraction, this is $\frac{20}{80}$ or $\frac{1}{4}$ of the total. So, as a rough estimate, the probability of your finding a particular book is 0.25 or 25%.

Similarly, 16 000 out of the total of 80 000 books are on unauthorised loan, a euphemism for *stolen,* and this is 20%, or $\frac{1}{5}$.

An important assumption underlying these calculations is that all the books are equally likely to be unavailable, which is not very realistic since popular books are more likely to be stolen. Also, the numbers given are only rough approximations, so it is definitely incorrect to say that the probability is *exactly* $\frac{1}{4}$.

Measuring probability

Probability (or chance) is a way of describing the likelihood of different possible *outcomes* occurring as a result of some *experiment.*

In the example of the library books, the experiment is looking in the library for a particular book. Let us assume that you already know that the book you want is on the library's stocks. The three possible outcomes are that the book is on the shelves, out on loan or missing.

It is important in probability to distinguish experiments from the outcomes which they may generate. Here are a few examples.

Experiments	Possible outcomes
• guessing the answer to a four-option multiple choice question	A
	B
	C
	D
• predicting the stamp on the next letter I receive	first class
	second class
	foreign
	other
• tossing a coin	heads
	tails

Another word for experiment is *trial.* This is used in Chapters 6 and 7 of this book to describe the binomial situation where there are just two possible outcomes.

Another word you should know is *event.* This often describes several outcomes put together. For example, when rolling a die, an event could be 'the die shows an even number'. This event corresponds to three different outcomes from the trial, the die showing 2, 4 or 6. However, the term event is also often used to describe a single outcome.

Estimating probability

Probability is a number which measures likelihood. It may be estimated experimentally or theoretically.

Experimental estimation of probability

In many situations probabilities are estimated on the basis of data collected experimentally, as in the following example.

Of 30 drawing pins tossed in the air, 21 of them were found to have landed with their pins pointing up. From this you would estimate the probability that the next pin tossed in the air will land with its pin pointing up to be $\frac{21}{30}$ or 0.7.

You can describe this in more formal notation.

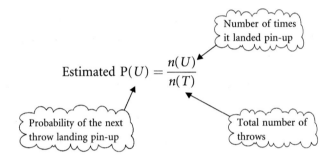

$$\text{Estimated } P(U) = \frac{n(U)}{n(T)}$$

Theoretical estimation of probability

There are, however, some situations where you do not need to collect data to make an estimate of probability.

For example, when tossing a coin, common sense tells you that there are only two realistic outcomes and, given the symmetry of the coin, you would expect them to be equally likely. So the probability, $P(H)$, that the next coin will produce the outcome heads can be written as follows:

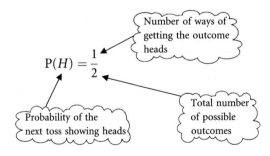

$$P(H) = \frac{1}{2}$$

EXAMPLE 3.1

Using the notation described above, write down the probability that the correct answer for the next four-option multiple choice question will be answer A. What assumptions are you making?

SOLUTION

Assuming that the test-setter has used each letter equally often, the probability, P(A), that the next question will have answer A can be written as follows:

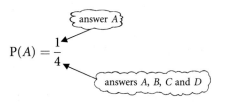

$$P(A) = \frac{1}{4}$$

Notice that we have assumed that the four options are equally likely. Equiprobability is an important assumption underlying most work on probability.

Expressed formally, the probability, P(A), of event A occurring is:

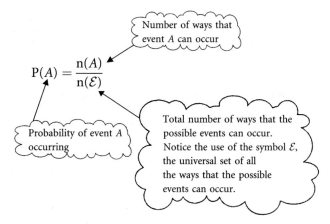

$$P(A) = \frac{n(A)}{n(\mathcal{E})}$$

Probabilities of 0 and 1

The two extremes of probability are *certainty* at one end of the scale and *impossibility* at the other. Here are examples of certain and impossible events.

Experiments	Certain events	Impossible event
• tossing a single die	the result is in the range 1 to 6 inclusive	the result is a 7
• tossing a coin	getting either heads or tails	getting neither heads nor tails

CERTAINTY

As you can see from the table above, for events that are certain, the number of ways that the event can occur, $n(A)$ in the formula, is equal to the total number of possible events, $n(\mathcal{E})$.

$$\frac{n(A)}{n(\mathcal{E})} = 1$$

So the probability of an event which is certain is 1.

IMPOSSIBILITY

For impossible events, the number of ways that the event can occur, $n(A)$, is zero.

$$\frac{n(A)}{n(\mathcal{E})} = \frac{0}{n(\mathcal{E})} = 0$$

So the probability of an event which is impossible is 0.

Typical values of probabilities might be something like 0.3 or 0.9. If you arrive at probability values of, say, -0.4 or 1.7, you will know that you have made a mistake since these are meaningless.

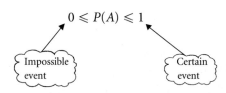

$$0 \leqslant P(A) \leqslant 1$$

Impossible event   Certain event

The complement of an event

The complement of an event A, denoted by A', is the event *not-A*, that is the event 'A does not happen'.

EXAMPLE 3.2

It was found that, out of a box of 50 matches, 45 lit but the others did not. What was the probability that a randomly selected match would not have lit?

SOLUTION

The probability that a randomly selected match lit was

$$P(A) = \frac{45}{50} = 0.9.$$

The probability that a randomly selected match did not light was

$$P(A') = \frac{(50 - 45)}{50} = \frac{5}{50} = 0.1.$$

From this example you can see that

$$P(A') = 1 - P(A)$$

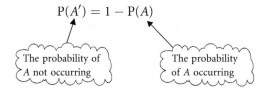

The probability of
A not occurring

The probability
of *A* occurring

This is illustrated in figure 3.1.

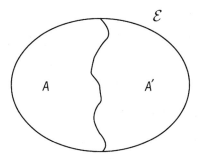

Figure 3.1 *Venn diagram showing events* A *and Not-A (A')*

Expectation

How many people can the Health Area expect to contract flu? The answer is easily seen to be $120\,000 \times \frac{1}{3} = 40\,000$. This is called the *expectation* and is given in this case by np where n is the population size and p the probability.

Expectation is a technical term and need not be a whole number. Thus the expectation of the number of heads when a coin is tossed 5 times is $5 \times \frac{1}{2} = 2.5$. You would be wrong to go on to say 'That means either 2 or 3' or to qualify your answer as 'about $2\frac{1}{2}$'. The expectation is 2.5.

Expectation is often used in the context of winnings from a gambling game.

EXAMPLE 3.3

In a raffle 500 tickets are sold for £1 each. There are five winning tickets. One ticket wins the first prize of £50, the other four each win a prize of £20. What are the expected winnings from buying a ticket?

SOLUTION

$$\text{Expected winnings} = £(50 \times \tfrac{1}{500} + 20 \times \tfrac{4}{500}) = £0.26$$

Since a ticket costs £1, anybody buying tickets can expect to lose on average 74p for each ticket they buy.

The probability of either one event or another

So far we have looked at just one event at a time. However, it is often useful to bracket two or more of the events together and calculate their combined probability.

EXAMPLE 3.4

The table below is based on the data at the beginning of this chapter and shows the probability of the next book requested falling into each of the three categories listed, assuming that each book is equally likely to be requested.

Category of book	Typical numbers	Probability
On the shelves (S)	20 000	0.25
Out on loan (L)	44 000	0.55
Unauthorised loan (U)	16 000	0.20
Total ($S + L + U$)	80 000	1.00

What is the probability that a randomly requested book is *either* out on loan *or* on unauthorised loan (i.e. that it is not available)?

SOLUTION

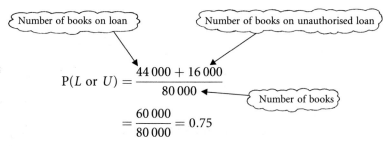

$$P(L \text{ or } U) = \frac{44\,000 + 16\,000}{80\,000}$$

$$= \frac{60\,000}{80\,000} = 0.75$$

This can be written in more formal notation as

$$P(L \cup U) = \frac{n(L \cup U)}{n(\mathcal{E})} = \frac{n(L)}{n(\mathcal{E})} + \frac{n(L)}{n(\mathcal{E})}$$

$$P(L \cup U) = P(L) + P(U)$$

Notice the use of the *union* symbol, ∪, to mean *or*. This is illustrated in figure 3.2.

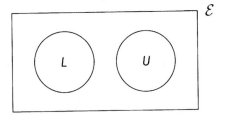

Key: L = out on loan
U = out on unauthorised loan

Figure 3.2 *Venn diagram showing events L and U. It is not possible for both to occur*

In this example you could add the probabilities of the two events to get the combined probability of *either one or the other* event occurring. However, you have to be very careful adding probabilities as you will see in the next example.

EXAMPLE 3.5

Below are further details of the categories of books in the library.

Category of book	Number of books
On the shelves	20 000
Out on loan	44 000
Adult fiction	22 000
Adult non-fiction	40 000
Junior	18 000
Unauthorised loan	16 000
Total stock	80 000

Assuming all the books in the library are equally likely to be requested, find the probability that the next book requested will be either out on loan or a book of adult non-fiction.

SOLUTION

$$P(\text{on loan}) + P(\text{adult non-fiction}) = \frac{44\,000}{80\,000} + \frac{40\,000}{80\,000}$$

$$= 0.55 + 0.5 = 1.05$$

This is clearly nonsense as you cannot have a probability greater than 1.

So what has gone wrong?

The way this calculation was carried out involved some double counting. Some of the books classed as adult non-fiction were counted twice because they were also in the on-loan category, as you can see from figure 3.3.

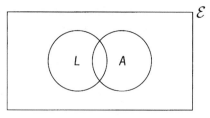

Key: L = out on loan
      A = adult non-fiction

Figure 3.3 *Venn diagram showing events* L *and* A. *It is possible for both to occur*

If you add all six of the book categories together, you find that they add up to 160 000, which represents twice the total number of books owned by the library.

A more useful representation of these data is given in the two-way table below.

	Adult fiction	Adult non-fiction	Junior	Total
On the shelves	4 000	12 000	4 000	20 000
Out on loan	14 000	20 000	10 000	44 000
Unauthorised loan	4 000	8 000	4 000	16 000
Total	22 000	40 000	18 000	80 000

If you simply add 44 000 and 40 000, you *double count* the 20 000 books which fall into both categories. So you need to subtract the 20 000 to ensure that it is counted only once. Thus:

Number either out on loan or adult non-fiction

$$= 44\,000 + 40\,000 - 20\,000$$
$$= 64\,000 \text{ books.}$$

So, the required probability $= \frac{64\,000}{80\,000} = 0.8.$

Mutually exclusive events

The problem of double counting does not occur when adding two rows in the table. Two rows cannot overlap, or *intersect*, which means that those categories are *mutually exclusive* (i.e. the one excludes the other). The same is true for two columns within the table.

Where two events, *A* and *B*, are mutually exclusive, the probability that either *A* or *B* occurs is equal to the sum of the separate probabilities of *A* and *B* occurring.

Where two events, *A* and *B*, are *not* mutually exclusive, the probability that either *A* or *B* occurs is equal to the sum of the separate probabilities of *A* and *B* occurring minus the probability of *A* and *B* occurring together.

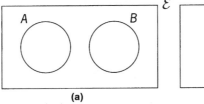 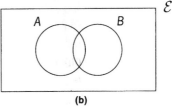

Figure 3.4 **(a)** *Mutually exclusive events;* **(b)** *Not mutually exclusive events*

$$P(A \cup B) = P(A) + P(B) \qquad P(A \cup B) = P(A) + P(B) - P(A \cap B)$$

> Notice the use of the intersection sign, ∩, to mean *both … and …*

EXAMPLE 3.6

A fair die is thrown. What is the probability that it shows

(i) Event A: an even number
(ii) Event B: a number greater than 4
(iii) Event $A \cup B$: a number which is either even or greater than 4?

SOLUTION

(i) Event A:
Three out of the six numbers on a die are even, namely 2, 4 and 6.
So $P(A) = \frac{3}{6} = \frac{1}{2}$.

(ii) Event B:
Two out of the six numbers on a die are greater than 4, namely 5 and 6.
So $P(B) = \frac{2}{6} = \frac{1}{3}$.

(iii) Event $A \cup B$:
Four of the numbers on a die are either even or greater than 4, namely 2, 4, 5 and 6.
So $P(A \cup B) = \frac{4}{6} = \frac{2}{3}$.

This could also be found using

$$P(A \cup B) = P(A) + P(B) - P(A \cap B)$$
$$P(A \cup B) = \frac{3}{6} + \frac{2}{6} - \frac{1}{6}$$
$$= \frac{4}{6} = \frac{2}{3}$$

> This is the number 6 which is both even and greater than 4.

EXERCISE 3A

1 Three separate electrical components, switch, bulb and contact point, are used together in the construction of a pocket torch. Of 534 defective torches, examined to identify the cause of failure, 468 are found to have a defective bulb. For a given failure of the torch, what is the probability that either the switch or the contact point is responsible for the failure? State clearly any assumptions that you have made in making this calculation.

2 If a fair die is thrown, what is the probability that it shows

(i) 4

(ii) 4 or more

(iii) less than 4

(iv) an even number?

3 A bag containing Scrabble letters has the following letter distribution

A	B	C	D	E	F	G	H	I	J	K	L	M
9	2	2	4	12	2	3	2	9	1	1	4	2

N	O	P	Q	R	S	T	U	V	W	X	Y	Z
6	8	2	1	6	4	6	4	2	2	1	2	1

The first letter is chosen at random from the bag; find the probability that it is

(i) an E

(ii) in the first half of the alphabet

(iii) in the second half of the alphabet

(iv) a vowel

(v) a consonant

(vi) the only one of its kind.

4 A lottery offers five prizes, each of £100, and a total of 2000 lottery tickets are sold. You buy a single ticket for 20p.

(i) What is the probability that you will win a prize?

(ii) What is the probability that you will not win a prize?

(iii) How much money do the lottery organisers expect to make or lose?

(iv) How much money should the lottery organisers charge for a single ticket in order to break even?

(v) If they continue to charge 20p per ticket, how many tickets would they need to sell in order to break even?

5 A sporting chance

(i) Two players, A and B, play tennis. On the basis of their previous results, the probability of A winning, P(A), is calculated to be 0.65. What is P(B), the probability of B winning?

(ii) Two hockey teams, A and B, play a game. On the basis of their previous results, the probability of team A winning, P(A), is calculated to be 0.65. Why is it not possible to calculate directly P(B), the probability of team B winning, without further information?

(iii) In a tennis tournament, player A, the favourite, is estimated to have a 0.3 chance of winning the competition. Player B is estimated to have a 0.15 chance. Find the probability that either A or B will win the competition.

(iv) In the Six Nations Rugby Championship, France and England are given a 25% chance of winning or sharing the championship cup. It is also estimated that there is a 5% chance that they will share the cup. Estimate the probability that either England or France will win or share the cup.

6 The integers 1 to 20 are classified as being either Even (*E*), Odd (*O*) or Square (*S*). (Some numbers are in more than one category.) They are written on separate identical cards and the cards are then thoroughly shuffled.

(i) Represent on a Venn diagram the possible outcomes of drawing a card at random.

(ii) A card is chosen at random. Find the probability that the number showing is:

(a) even, *E* **(b)** square, *S* **(c)** odd, *O*

(d) both even and square, $E \cap S$

(e) either even or square, $E \cup S$

(f) both even and odd, $E \cap O$

(g) either even or odd, $E \cup O$.

Write down equations connecting the probabilities of the following events:

(h) *E*, *S*, $E \cap S$, $E \cup S$

(i) *E*, *O*, $E \cap O$, $E \cup O$.

7 The data in the table below show the numbers of part-time students in higher education in 1988/89 by sex and type of establishment (numbers in thousands).

	Women	Men
Universities	21.1	29.0
Open University	40.3	45.0
Polytechnics and colleges		
– part-time day courses	67.0	118.5
– evening only courses	26.5	38.1
Total part-time students	154.9	230.6

(Source: *Education Statistics for the United Kingdom*, Department of Education and Science.)

Find the probability that a part-time student chosen at random is

(i) an Open University student

(ii) female

(iii) a female Open University student

(iv) studying at a polytechnic or college

(v) not studying at a polytechnic or college.

THE AVONFORD STAR

A Chance in a Million

I don't know whether Veronica, 14, saw a black cat last Saturday morning, or six magpies, or what, but it was certainly her lucky day.

Not only did her one and only ticket win her the top prize of £100 in the raffle at Avonford Summer Fair but later in the afternoon she received another £50 when her programme number came up in the programme draw.

Veronica said, 'To be honest, I didn't even know there was a programme draw. I was just about to throw mine away when they announced the winning number. I couldn't believe it — two wins in one day. It must be a chance in a million.'

This story describes two pieces of good fortune on the same day. Veronica said the probability was about $\frac{1}{1\,000\,000}$. What was it really?

The two events resulted from two different experiments, the raffle draw and the programme draw. Consequently this situation is different from those you met in the previous section. There you were looking at two events from a single experiment (like the number coming up when a die is thrown being even or being greater than 4).

The total sales of raffle tickets were 1245 and of programmes 324. The draws were conducted fairly, that is each number had an equal chance of being selected. The table below sets out the two experiments and their corresponding events with associated probabilities.

Experiment	Events (and estimated probabilities)
Raffle draw	Winning with a single ticket: $\frac{1}{1245}$ Not winning with a single ticket: $\frac{1244}{1245}$
Programme draw	Winning with a single programme: $\frac{1}{324}$ Not winning with a single programme: $\frac{323}{324}$

In situations like this the possible outcomes resulting from the different experiments are often shown on a *tree diagram*.

EXAMPLE 3.3

Find, in advance of the results of the two draws, the probability that

(i)   Veronica would win both draws
(ii) Veronica would fail to win either draw
(iii) Veronica would win one of the two draws.

SOLUTION

The possible results are shown on the tree diagram in figure 3.5.

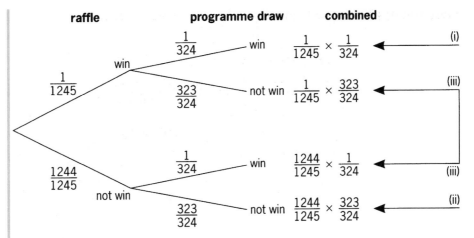

Figure 3.5

(i) The probability that Veronica wins both

$$= \frac{1}{1245} \times \frac{1}{324} = \frac{1}{403\,380}$$

This is not quite Veronica's 'one in a million' but it is not very far off it.

(ii) The probability that Veronica wins neither

$$= \frac{1244}{1245} \times \frac{323}{324} = \frac{401\,812}{403\,380}$$

This of course is much the most likely outcome.

(iii) The probability that Veronica wins one but not the other is given by

$$= \underbrace{\frac{1}{1245} \times \frac{323}{324}}_{} + \underbrace{\frac{1244}{1255} \times \frac{1}{234}}_{} = \frac{1567}{403\,380}$$

⎰ Wins raffle but ⎱   ⎰ Wins programme ⎱
⎱ not programme draw ⎰   ⎱ but not raffle draw ⎰

Look again at the structure of the tree diagram in figure 3.5.

There are two experiments, the raffle draw and the programme draw. These are considered as *First, Then* experiments, and set out *First* on the left and *Then* on the right. Once you understand this, the rest of the layout falls into place, with the different outcomes or events appearing as branches. In this example there are two branches at each stage; sometimes there may be three or more. Notice that for a given situation the component probabilities sum to 1, as before.

$$\frac{1}{403\,380} + \frac{323}{403\,380} + \frac{1244}{403\,380} + \frac{401\,812}{403\,380} = \frac{403\,380}{403\,380} = 1$$

EXAMPLE 3.8

Some friends buy a six-pack of potato crisps. Two of the bags are snake flavoured (S), the rest are frog flavoured (F). They decide to allocate the bags by lucky dip. Find the probability that

(i) the first two bags chosen are the same as each other

(ii) the first two bags chosen are different from each other.

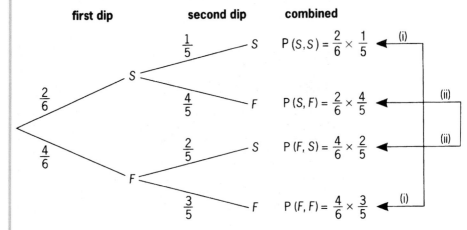

Figure 3.6

SOLUTION

Note: $P(F, S)$ means the probability of drawing a frog bag (F) on the first dip and a snake bag (S) on the second.

(i) The probability that the first two bags chosen are the same as each
other $= P(S, S) + P(F, F) = \frac{2}{6} \times \frac{1}{5} + \frac{4}{6} \times \frac{3}{5}$
$$= \frac{1}{15} + \frac{6}{15}$$
$$= \frac{7}{15}$$

(ii) The probability that the first two bags chosen are different from each
other $= P(S, F) + P(F, S) = \frac{2}{6} \times \frac{4}{5} + \frac{4}{6} \times \frac{2}{5}$
$$= \frac{4}{15} + \frac{4}{15}$$
$$= \frac{8}{15}$$

Note

The answer to part (ii) above hinged on the fact that two orderings (S then F, and F then S) are possible for the same combined event (that the two bags selected include one snake and one frog bag).

The probabilities changed between the first dip and the second dip. This is because the outcome of the second dip is *dependent* on the outcome of the first one (with fewer bags remaining to choose from).

By contrast, the outcomes of the two experiments involved in tossing a coin twice are *independent*, and so the probability of getting a head on the second toss remains unchanged at 0.5, whatever the outcome of the first toss.

Although you may find it helpful to think about combined events in terms of how they would be represented on a tree diagram, you may not always actually draw them in this way. If there are several experiments and perhaps more than two possible outcomes from each, drawing a tree diagram can be very time-consuming.

Calvin, a keen gambler, writes a regular article in the *Avonford Star* entitled 'Calvin's Tips'. This is one of them.

THE AVONFORD STAR

Calvin's Tips

I was playing roulette last night. The first time I bet on my lucky number 7 and lucky it was. I then put all my winnings on my other lucky number, 4. That came up too so I collected my winnings and moved off to a poker table.

When I came back later I found my friend Katy still at the roulette table, looking very cross. 'My lucky number is 17 and I have tried it 40 times and not once has it come up,' she explained. 'I'm jinxed. I would have expected to win twice by now and that would make me £32 up not £40 down.'

I know I was lucky, but was Katy really that unlucky? Did she have good reason to think herself jinxed?

A roulette wheel has 37 numbers marked on it $(0, 1, 2, 3, \ldots, 36)$ so the probability that your number comes up on any roll is $\frac{1}{37}$.

On one roll,

$$P(\text{win}) = \tfrac{1}{37} \quad P(\text{not win}) = 1 - \tfrac{1}{37} = \tfrac{36}{37}.$$

On 40 rolls,

$$P(\text{no wins}) = \tfrac{36}{37} \times \tfrac{36}{37} \times \tfrac{36}{37} \times \cdots \times \tfrac{36}{37} = \left(\tfrac{36}{37}\right)^{40}$$
$$= 0.334.$$

So no wins in 40 rolls is not particularly unlikely. Katy has no reason to think herself jinxed.

The probability of Calvin's outcome is $\frac{1}{37} \times \frac{1}{37} = 0.000\,73$. This is a low probability and he is quite right to think himself lucky.

The odds offered by most casinos for a single number are 35–1, meaning that if you bet £1 you win £35 and get your £1 back.

So on one roll the expectation of your winnings is

$$£\left(35 \times \tfrac{1}{37} - 1 \times \tfrac{36}{37}\right) = -2.7\text{p, or a 2.7p loss.}$$

On 40 rolls Katy could expect to lose $40 \times 2.7\text{p} = £1.08$.

In fact she had lost £40 so perhaps she was entitled to think that luck was not on her side, but her statement that she should be £32 in profit was certainly not accurate.

THE AVONFORD STAR

Is this justice?

In 1991, local man David Starr was sentenced to 12 years' imprisonment for armed robbery solely on the basis of an identification parade. He was one of 12 people in the parade and was picked out by one witness but not by three others.

Many Avonford people who knew David well believe he was incapable of such a crime. We in the Star are now adding our voice to the clamour for a review of his case.

How conclusive, we ask, is this sort of evidence, or, to put it another way, how likely is it that a mistake has been made?

Investigate the likelihood that David Starr really did commit the robbery.

SOLUTION

In this situation you need to assess the probability of an innocent individual being picked out by chance alone. Assume that David Starr was innocent and the witnesses were selecting in a purely random way (that is, with a probability of $\frac{1}{12}$ of selecting each person and a probability of $\frac{11}{12}$ of not selecting each person). If each of the witnesses selected just one of the twelve people in the identity parade in this random manner, how likely is it that David Starr would be picked out by at least one witness?

P(at least one selection) $= 1 - $ P(no selections)

$$= 1 - \tfrac{11}{12} \times \tfrac{11}{12} \times \tfrac{11}{12} \times \tfrac{11}{12}$$

$$= 1 - 0.706 = 0.294 \text{ (i.e. roughly 30\%)}.$$

In other words, there is about a 30% chance of an innocent person being chosen in this way by at least one of the witnesses.

The newspaper article concluded:

THE AVONFORD STAR

Is 30% really the sort of figure we have in mind when judges use the phrase 'beyond reasonable doubt'? Because if it is, many innocent people will be condemned to a life behind bars.

This raises an important statistical idea, which you will meet again in Chapter 7, about how we make judgements and decisions.

Judgements are usually made under conditions of uncertainty and involve us in having to weigh up the plausibility of one explanation against that of another. Statistical judgements are usually made on such a basis. We choose one explanation if we judge the alternative explanation to be sufficiently unlikely, that is if the probability of its being true is sufficiently small. Exactly how small this probability has to be will depend on the individual circumstances and is called the *significance level*.

Somebody on trial is assumed innocent until shown to be guilty beyond reasonable doubt; reasonable doubt must mean a very small probability that the person is innocent.

1 The probability of a pregnant woman giving birth to a baby girl is about 0.49. Draw a tree diagram showing the possible outcomes if she has two babies (not twins). From the tree diagram, calculate the following probabilities:
   (i)   that the babies are both girls
   (ii) that the babies are the same sex
   (iii) that the second baby is of different sex to the first.

2 In a certain district of a large city, the probability of a household suffering a break-in in a particular year is 0.07 and the probability of its car being stolen is 0.12. Assuming these two trials are independent of each other, draw a tree diagram showing the possible outcomes for a particular year. Calculate, for a randomly selected household with one car, the following probabilities:
   (i)   that the household is a victim of both crimes during that year
   (ii) that the household suffers *only one* of these misfortunes during that year
   (iii) that the household suffers *at least one* of these misfortunes during that year.

3 There are 12 people at an identification parade. Three witnesses are called to identify the accused person. Assuming they make their choice purely by random selection, draw a tree diagram showing the possible events.
   (i) From the tree diagram, calculate the following probabilities:
       (a) that all three witnesses select the accused person
       (b) that none of the witnesses selects the accused person
       (c) that at least two of the witnesses select the accused person.
   (ii) Suppose now that by changing the composition of people in the identification parade, the first two witnesses increase their chances of selecting the accused person to 0.25. Draw a new tree diagram and calculate the following probabilities:
       (a) that all three witnesses select the accused person
       (b) that none of the witnesses selects the accused person
       (c) that at least two of the witnesses select the accused person.

4 Ruth drives her car to work – provided she can get it to start! When she remembers to put the car in the garage the night before, it starts next morning with a probability of 0.95. When she forgets to put the car away, it starts next morning with a probability of 0.75. She remembers to garage her car 90% of the time.

What is the probability that Ruth drives her car to work on a randomly chosen day?

5   Around 0.8% of men are red–green colour-blind (the figure is slightly different for women) and roughly 1 in 5 men is left-handed. Assuming these characteristics are inherited independently, calculate with the aid of a tree diagram the probability that a man chosen at random will
   (i)   be both colour-blind and left-handed
   (ii) be colour-blind and not left-handed
   (iii) be colour-blind or left-handed
   (iv) be neither colour-blind nor left-handed.

6   A gambling game consists of tossing a coin three times. You win if all three tosses give the same result (i.e. three heads or three tails) and you lose if any other event shows. Calculate the probability that you will lose a particular game.

7   All the Jacks, Queens and Kings are removed from a pack of cards. Giving the Ace a value of 1, this leaves a pack of 40 cards consisting of four suits of cards numbered 1 to 10. The cards are well shuffled and one is drawn and noted. This card is not returned to the pack and a second card is drawn. Find the probability that
   (i)   both cards are even
   (ii) at least one card is odd
   (iii) both cards are of the same suit
   (iv) only one of the cards has a value greater than 7.

8   Three dice are thrown. Find the probability of obtaining
   (i)   at least two 6s
   (ii) no 6s
   (iii) different scores on all the dice.

9   Explain the flaw in this argument and rewrite it as a valid statement.
   The probability of throwing a 6 on a fair die $= \frac{1}{6}$. Therefore the probability of throwing at least one 6 in six throws of the die is $\frac{1}{6} + \frac{1}{6} + \frac{1}{6} + \frac{1}{6} + \frac{1}{6} + \frac{1}{6} = 1$ so it is a certainty.

10 In a Donkey Derby event, there are three races. There are six donkeys entered for the first race, four for the second and three the third. Sheila places a bet on one donkey in each race. She knows nothing about donkeys and chooses each donkey at random. Find the probability that she backs at least one winner.

11 Two dice are thrown, one red and the other green.

(i) Copy and complete this table showing all the possible outcomes.

		Green die					
+		1	2	3	4	5	6
Red die	1						
	2						
	3						
	4						10
	5						11
	6	7	8	9	10	11	12

(ii) What is the probability of a score of 4?

(iii) What is the most likely outcome?

(iv) Criticise this argument:

There are 11 possible outcomes, 2, 3, 4, up to 12. Therefore each of them has a probability of $\frac{1}{11}$.

12 A gambling game consists of tossing a coin three times. If two or more heads show, you get your money back. If you throw three heads, you receive double your stake money. Otherwise you lose. For a single throw, calculate

(i) the probability of losing your money

(ii) the probability of doubling your money

(iii) the probability of just getting your money back

(iv) the expectation of the value of your winnings, given a £1 stake.

13 The probability of someone catching flu in a particular winter when they have been given the flu vaccine is 0.1. Without the vaccine, the probability of catching flu is 0.4. If 30% of the population has been given the vaccine, what is the probability that a person chosen at random from the population will catch flu over that winter.

14 In a gambling game, players pay an entry fee of £1. They then throw a die until it shows 6. If only one throw is needed, the player receives £3. If two throws are needed, the player receives £2. If three throws are needed, the player gets his or her entry fee back; otherwise the £1 is lost. Find the probability that a player

(i) receives £3

(ii) receives £2

(iii) gets the £1 entry fee back

(iv) loses the entry fee.

15 Kevin hosts the TV programme *Thank Your Lucky Stars*. During the show he picks members of the large studio audience at random and asks them what star sign they were born under.

(There are 12 star signs in all and you may assume that the probabilities that a randomly chosen person will be born under each star sign are equal.)

(i) The first person Kevin picks says that he was born under the star sign Aries. What is the probability that the next person he picks was *not* born under Aries?

(ii) Show that the probability that the first three people picked were all born under different star signs is approximately 0.764.

(iii) Calculate the probability that the first five people picked were all born under different star signs.

(iv) What is the probability that at least two of the first five people picked were born under the same star sign?

[MEI (part)]

16 One plastic toy aeroplane is given away free in each packet of cornflakes. Equal numbers of red, yellow, green and blue aeroplanes are put into the packets.

Faye, a customer, has collected three colours of aeroplane but still wants a yellow one. Find the probability that

(i) she gets a yellow aeroplane by opening just one packet

(ii) she fails to get a yellow aeroplane in opening four packets

(iii) she needs to open **exactly** five packets to get the yellow aeroplane she wants.

Henry, a quality controller employed by the cornflakes manufacturer, opens a number chosen at random to check on the distribution of colours. Find the probability that

(iv) the first two packets he opens both have red aeroplanes in

(v) the first two packets he opens have aeroplanes of different colours in

(vi) he gets all four different colours by opening just four packets.

[MEI]

Conditional probability

THE AVONFORD STAR

Local man dies of heart attack

Mr Paul Strangelove, 47, of Dunrobbin Close, collapsed while out shopping late yesterday afternoon. He was rushed to hospital but found to be dead on arrival.

What is the probability that somebody chosen at random will die of a heart attack in the next 12 months?

One approach would be to say that, since there are about 300 000 deaths per year from heart and circulatory diseases (H & CD) among the 57 000 000 population of the UK,

$$\text{probability} = \frac{\text{Number of deaths from H \& CD per year in UK}}{\text{Total population of UK}}$$

$$= \frac{300\,000}{57\,000\,000} = 0.0053$$

However, if you think about it, you will probably realise that this is rather a meaningless figure. For a start, young people are much less at risk than those in or beyond middle age.

So you might wish to give two answers:

$$P_1 = \frac{\text{Deaths from H \& CD among over-40s}}{\text{Population of over-40s}}$$

$$P_2 = \frac{\text{Deaths from H \& CD among under-40s}}{\text{Population of under-40s}}$$

Typically only 1500 of the deaths would be among the under-40s leaving (on the basis of these figures) 298 500 among the over-40s. About 25 000 000 people in the UK are over 40, and 32 000 000 under 40 (40 years and 1 day counts as over 40). This gives

$$P_1 = \frac{\text{Deaths from H \& CD among over-40s}}{\text{Population of over-40s}} = \frac{298\,500}{25\,000\,000}$$

$$= 0.0119$$

and

$$P_2 = \frac{\text{Deaths from H \& CD among under-40s}}{\text{Population of under-40s}} = \frac{1500}{32\,000\,000}$$

$$= 0.000\,47$$

So somebody in the older group is over 200 times more likely to die of a heart attack than somebody in the younger group. Putting them both together as an average figure resulted in a figure that was representative of neither group. (The figures used in this section are approximated from those supplied by the British Heart Foundation who had themselves used a number of official sources.)

But why stop there? You could, if you had the figures, divide population up into 10-year, 5-year, or even 1-year intervals. That would certainly improve the accuracy; but there are also more factors that you might wish to take into account.

- Is the person overweight?
- Does the person smoke?
- Does the person take regular exercise?
  etc.

The more conditions you build in, the more accurate will be the estimate of the probability.

You can see how the conditions are brought in by looking at P_1:

$$P_1 = \frac{\text{Deaths from H \& CD among over-40s}}{\text{Population of over-40s}} = \frac{298\,500}{25\,000\,000}$$

$$= 0.0119$$

You would write this in symbols as follows:

Event G: Somebody selected at random is over 40.
Event H: Somebody selected at random dies from H & CD.

The probability of someone dying from H & CD given that he or she is over 40 is given by the conditional probability $P(H \mid G)$ where

$$P(H \mid G) = \frac{n(H \cap G)}{n(G)}$$

$$= \frac{n(H \cap G)/n(\mathcal{E})}{n(G)/n(\mathcal{E})}$$

$$= \frac{P(H \cap G)}{P(G)}$$

$P(H \mid G)$ means the probability of event H occurring *given that* event G has occurred

This result may be written in general form for all cases of conditional probability for events A and B

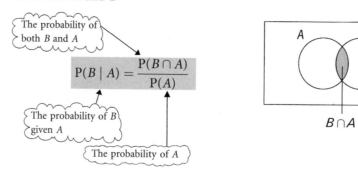

The probability of both B and A

$$P(B \mid A) = \frac{P(B \cap A)}{P(A)}$$

The probability of B given A

The probability of A

$B \cap A$

Conditional probability is used when your estimate of the probability of an event is altered by your knowledge of whether some other event has occurred. In this case the estimate of the probability of somebody dying from heart and circulatory diseases, $P(H)$, is altered by a knowledge of whether the person is over 40 or not.

Thus conditional probability addresses the question of whether one event is dependent on another one. If the probability of event B is not affected by the occurrence of event A, we say that B is *independent* of A. If, on the other hand, the probability of event B is affected by the occurrence (or not) of event A, we say that B is *dependent* on A.

If A and B are independent, then $P(B \mid A) = P(B \mid A')$ and this is just $P(B)$.

If A and B are dependent, then $P(B \mid A) \neq P(B \mid A')$.

As you have already seen, the probability of a combined event is the product of the separate probabilities of each event, provided the question of dependence between the two events is properly dealt with. Specifically:

The probability of both A and B occurring

For dependent events $P(A \cap B) = P(A) \times P(B \mid A)$

The probability of A occurring

The probability of B occurring, given that A has occurred

When A and B are independent events, then, because $P(B \mid A) = P(B)$, this can be written as

For independent events $P(A \cap B) = P(A) \times P(B)$

EXAMPLE 3.10

A company is worried about the high turnover of its employees and decides to investigate whether they are more likely to stay if they are given training.

On 1 January one year the company employed 256 people (excluding those about to retire). During that year a record was kept of who received training as well as who left the company. The results are summarised in this table:

	Still employed	Left company	
Given training	109	43	152
Not given training	60	44	104
	169	87	256

Find the probability that a randomly selected employee
(i) received training
(ii) did not leave the company
(iii) received training and did not leave the company
(iv) did not leave the company, given that the person had received training
(v) did not leave the company, given that the person had not received training.

SOLUTION

Using the notation T: The employee received training
$\qquad\qquad\quad\;$ S: The employee stayed in the company

(i) $\qquad\qquad P(T) = \dfrac{n(T)}{n(\mathcal{E})} = \frac{152}{256}$

(ii) $\qquad\qquad P(S) = \dfrac{n(S)}{n(\mathcal{E})} = \frac{169}{256}$

(iii) $\qquad P(T \cap S) = \dfrac{n(T \cap S)}{n(\mathcal{E})} = \frac{109}{256}$

(iv) $\qquad P(S \mid T) = \dfrac{P(S \cap T)}{P(T)} = \dfrac{\frac{109}{256}}{\frac{152}{256}} = \frac{109}{152} = 0.72$

(v) $\qquad P(S \mid T') = \dfrac{P(S \cap T')}{P(T')} = \dfrac{\frac{60}{256}}{\frac{104}{256}} = \frac{60}{104} = 0.58$

Since $P(S \mid T)$ is not the same as $P(S \mid T')$, the event S is not independent of the event T. Each of S and T is dependent on the other, a conclusion which matches common sense. It is almost certainly true that training increases employees' job satisfaction and so makes them more likely to stay, but it is also probably true that the company is more likely to go to the expense of training the employees who seem less inclined
to move on to other jobs.

? How would you show that the event T is not independent of the event S.

In some situations you may find it helps to represent a problem such as this as a

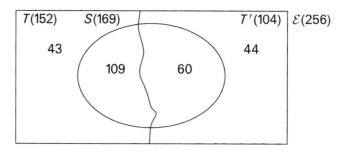

Figure 3.7

Venn diagram.

? What do the various numbers and letters represent?
Where is the region S'?
How are the numbers on the diagram related to the answers to parts (i) to (v)?

In other situations it may be helpful to think of conditional probabilities in terms of tree diagrams. Conditional probabilities are needed when events are *dependent,* that is when the outcome of one trial affects the outcomes from a subsequent trial, so, for dependent events, the probabilities of all but the first layer of a tree diagram will be conditional.

EXAMPLE 3.11 Rebecca is buying two goldfish from a pet shop. The shop's tank contains seven male fish and eight female fish but they all look the same.

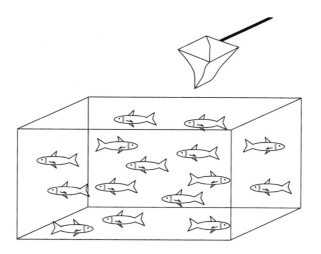

Figure 3.8

Find the probability that Rebecca's fish are
(i)   both the same sex
(ii) both female
(iii) both female given that they are the same sex.

SOLUTION

The situation is shown on this tree diagram.

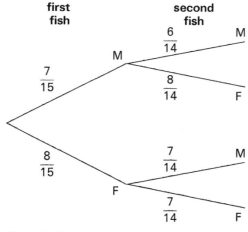

$$P(\text{both male}) = \frac{7}{15} \times \frac{6}{14} = \frac{42}{210}$$

$$P(\text{male, female}) = \frac{7}{15} \times \frac{8}{14} = \frac{56}{210}$$

$$P(\text{female, male}) = \frac{8}{15} \times \frac{7}{14} = \frac{56}{210}$$

$$P(\text{both female}) = \frac{8}{15} \times \frac{7}{14} = \frac{56}{210}$$

Figure 3.9

(i) P(both the same sex) = P(both male) + P(both female)

$$= \frac{42}{210} + \frac{56}{210} = \frac{98}{210} = \frac{7}{15}$$

(ii) P(both female) = $\dfrac{56}{210} = \dfrac{4}{15}$

(iii) P(both female | both the same sex)

$$= \text{P(both female and the same sex)/P(both the same sex)} = \frac{\frac{4}{15}}{\frac{7}{15}} = \frac{4}{7}$$

> This is the same as P(both female)

The ideas in the last example can be expressed more generally for any two dependent events, A and B. The tree diagram would be as shown in figure 3.10.

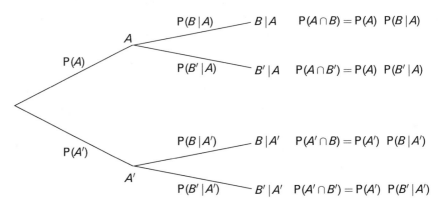

Figure 3.10

> The probabilities in the second layer of the tree diagram are conditional on the outcome of the first experiment

> These events are conditional upon the outcome of the first experiment

The tree diagram shows you that

- P(B) = P(A ∩ B) + P(A′ ∩ B)
  = P(A)P(B | A) + P(A′)P(B | A′)

- P(A ∩ B) = P(A)P(B | A)
  ⇒ P(B | A) = $\dfrac{\text{P}(A \cap B)}{\text{P}(A)}$

❓ How were these results used in Example 3.11 about the goldfish?

1 In a school of 600 pupils, 360 are girls. There are 320 hockey players, of whom 200 are girls. Among the hockey players there are 28 goalkeepers, 19 of them girls. Find the probability that

  (i) a pupil chosen at random is a girl
  (ii) a girl chosen at random plays hockey
  (iii) a hockey player chosen at random is a girl
  (iv) a pupil chosen at random is a goalkeeper
  (v) a goalkeeper chosen at random is a boy
  (vi) a male hockey player chosen at random is a goalkeeper
  (vii) a hockey player chosen at random is a male goalkeeper
  (viii) two pupils chosen at random are both goalkeepers
  (ix) two pupils chosen at random are a male goalkeeper and a female goalkeeper
  (x) two pupils chosen at random are one boy and one girl.

2 The table below gives the numbers of offenders in England and Wales sentenced for indictable offences, by type of offence and type of sentence, in 1989 (numbers in thousands).

	Discharge	Probation	Fine	Jail	Other	Total
Violence	9.5	3.9	20.6	9.0	12.7	55.7
Sexual offences	0.8	0.9	2.4	2.4	0.8	7.3
Theft	31.4	26.2	62.6	29.9	32.1	182.2
Motoring	0.5	0.3	8.7	1.0	0.8	11.3
Other	12.0	9.4	41.3	11.9	7.9	82.5
Total	54.2	40.7	135.6	54.2	54.3	339.0

(Source: adapted from Table 12.19, *Social Trends* 22, 1992, CSO.)

(i) Find the probability that a randomly selected person indicted for an offence will be

  (a) discharged **(b)** put on probation
  (c) fined   **(d)** sent to jail
  (e) sent to jail for a motoring offence
  (f) sent to jail given that the person has committed a motoring offence
  (g) guilty of a motoring offence given that the person is sent to jail.

(ii) Criticise this statement:
  Based on these figures nearly 2% of the country's prison population are there for motoring offences.

3 100 cars are entered for a road-worthiness test which is in two parts, mechanical and electrical. A car passes only if it passes both parts. Half the cars fail the electrical test and 62 pass the mechanical. 15 pass the electrical but fail the mechanical test. Find the probability that a car chosen at random

(i) passes overall

(ii) fails on one test only

(iii) given that it has failed, failed the mechanical test only.

4 Two dice are thrown. What is the probability that the total is

(i) 7

(ii) a prime number

(iii) 7, given that it is a prime number?

5 A cage holds two litters of rats. One litter comprises three females and four males, and the other comprises two females and six males. A random selection of two rats is made. Find, as fractions, the probabilities that the two rats are

(i) from the same litter

(ii) of the same sex

(iii) from the same litter and of the same sex

(iv) from the same litter given that they are of the same sex.

[MEI]

6 In a school of 400 pupils, 250 play a musical instrument and 100 sing in the choir.

The probability that a pupil chosen at random neither plays a musical instrument nor sings in the choir is $\frac{1}{5}$.

(i) How many pupils both sing in the choir and play a musical instrument?

(ii) Find the probability that a pupil chosen at random sings in the choir but does not play an instrument.

(iii) Find the probability that a member of the choir chosen at random does not play an instrument.

(iv) Find the probability that someone who does not play an instrument, chosen at random, is in the choir.

7 A bag P contains three red balls. A second bag Q contains two red balls and three black balls.

(i) A bag is chosen at random and one ball is withdrawn. Find the probability that this ball is red.

This ball remains outside the bag.

(ii) A bag is again chosen at random (it is not known whether this is the same bag as before or not) and one ball is withdrawn. Find the joint probability that both this ball and the one previously withdrawn are red.

(iii) If they are both red, what is the probability that bag P was used on both occasions?

[O & C]

8 In a child's game there should be seven triangles, three of which are blue and four of which are red, and eleven squares, five of which are blue and six of which are red. However, two pieces are lost. Assuming the pieces are lost at random, find the probability that they are
   (i) the same shape
   (ii) the same colour
   (iii) the same shape and the same colour
   (iv) the same shape given that they are the same colour.

[MEI]

9 *A* and *B* are two events with probabilities given by $P(A) = 0.4$, $P(B) = 0.7$ and $P(A \cap B) = 0.35$.
   (i) Find $P(A \mid B)$ and $P(B \mid A)$.
   (ii) Show that the events *A* and *B* are not independent.

10 Quark hunting is a dangerous occupation. On a quark hunt, there is a probability of $\frac{1}{4}$ that the hunter is killed. The quark is twice as likely to be killed as the hunter. There is a probability of $\frac{1}{3}$ that both survive.
   (i) Copy and complete this table of probabilities.

	Hunter dies	Hunter lives	
Quark dies			$\frac{1}{2}$
Quark lives		$\frac{1}{3}$	$\frac{1}{2}$
	$\frac{1}{4}$		1

Find the probability that
   (ii) both the hunter and the quark die
   (iii) the hunter lives and the quark dies
   (iv) the hunter lives, given that the quark dies.

11 In a tea shop 70% of customers order tea with milk, 20% tea with lemon and 10% tea with neither. Of those taking tea with milk $\frac{3}{5}$ take sugar, of those taking tea with lemon $\frac{1}{4}$ take sugar, and of those taking tea with neither milk nor lemon $\frac{11}{20}$ take sugar. A customer is chosen at random.
   (i) Represent the information given on a tree diagram and use it to find the probability that the customer takes sugar.
   (ii) Find the probability that the customer takes milk or sugar or both.
   (iii) Find the probability that the customer takes sugar *and* milk. Hence find the probability that the customer takes milk *given that* the customer takes sugar.

[MEI]

12 Every year two teams, the *Ramblers* and the *Strollers*, meet each other for a quiz night. From past results it seems that in years when the *Ramblers* win, the probability of them winning the next year is 0.7 and in years when the *Strollers* win, the probability of them winning the next year is 0.5. It is not possible for the quiz to result in the scores being tied.

The *Ramblers* won the quiz in 1996.

(i) Draw a probability tree diagram for the three years up to 1999.

(ii) Find the probability that the *Strollers* will win in 1999.

(iii) If the *Strollers* win in 1999, what is the probability that it will be their first win for at least three years?

(iv) Assuming that the *Strollers* win in 1999, find the smallest value of n such that the probability of the *Ramblers* winning the quiz for n consecutive years after 1999 is less than 5%.

[MEI]

13 On my way home from work each evening I have to pass through three sets of traffic lights in the city centre. The probabilities that I pass through them *without* having to stop are 0.2, 0.4 and 0.7 respectively. You may assume that each set of lights operates independently of the others.

(i) Draw a tree diagram to illustrate the situation.

(ii) Find the probability that I do not have to stop at any of the three sets of lights.

(iii) Find the probability that I have to stop at just one set of lights.

(iv) Given that I have to stop at just one set of lights, find the probability that I have to stop at the first set of lights.

(v) It is decided to change the probability of passing through the first lights without having to stop from 0.2 to p. I find that this change reduces the probability found in part (iv) to 0.5. Calculate p.

[MEI]

14 There are 90 players in a tennis club. Of these, 23 are juniors, the rest are seniors. 34 of the seniors and 10 of the juniors are male. There are 8 juniors who are left-handed, 5 of whom are male. There are 18 left-handed players in total, 4 of whom are female seniors.

(i) Represent this information in a Venn diagram.

(ii) What is the probability that

(a) a male player selected at random is left-handed?

(b) a left-handed player selected at random is a female junior?

(c) a player selected at random is either a junior or a female?

(d) a player selected at random is right-handed?

(e) a right-handed player selected at random is not a junior?

(f) a right-handed female player selected at random is a junior?

1 The probability of an event A, $P(A) = n(A)/n(\mathcal{E})$, where $n(A)$ is the number of ways that A can occur and $n(\mathcal{E})$ is the total number of ways that all possible events can occur, all of which are equally likely.

2 For any two events, A and B, of the same experiment,

$$P(A \cup B) = P(A) + P(B) - P(A \cap B).$$

Where the events are *mutually exclusive* (i.e. where the events do not overlap) the rule still holds but, since $P(A \cap B)$ is now equal to zero, the equation simplifies to:

$$P(A \cap B) = P(A) + P(B).$$

3 Where an experiment produces two or more mutually exclusive events, the probabilities of the separate events sum to 1.

4 $P(A) + P(A') = 1$

5 $P(B \mid A)$ means the probability of event B occurring given that event A has already occurred.

$$P(B \mid A) = \frac{P(A \cap B)}{P(A)}$$

6 The probability that event A and then event B occur, in that order, is $P(A) \times P(B \mid A)$.

7 If event B is independent of event A, $P(B \mid A) = P(B \mid A') = P(B)$.

Sampling

If you wish to learn swimming you have to go into the water.

G. Polya

THE AVONFORD STAR

Independent set to become Local M.P.

Next week's Avonford by-election looks set to produce the first independent Member of Parliament for many years, according to an opinion poll conducted by the Star's research team.

When 30 potential voters were asked who they thought would make the best M.P., 12 opted for Independent candidate Mrs Curtis. The other three candidates attracted between 3 and 9 votes.

Mrs Valerie Curtis taking the polls by storm.

Assuming that the figures quoted in the article are true, does this really mean that Independent Mrs Curtis will be elected to Parliament next week?

Only time will tell that, but meanwhile the newspaper report raises a number of questions that should make you suspicious of its conclusion.

Was the sample large enough? Thirty seems a very small number.

Were those interviewed asked the right question? They were asked who they thought would make the best M.P., not who they intended to vote for.

How was the sample selected? Was it representative of the whole electorate?

Before addressing these questions you will find it helpful to be familiar with the language and notation associated with sampling.

Terms and notation

The *Avonford Star* have taken a sample of size 30. Taking samples and interpreting them is an essential part of statistics. The populations in which you are interested are often so large that it would be quite impractical to use every item; the electorate of Avonford might well number 70 000.

A *sample* provides a set of data values of a random variable, drawn from all such possible values, the *parent population*. The parent population can be finite, such as all professional footballers, or infinite, such as the points where a dart can land on a dart board.

A representation of the items available to be sampled is called the *sampling frame*. This could, for example, be a list of the sheep in a flock, a map marked with a grid or an electoral register. In many situations no sampling frame exists nor is it possible to devise one, for example, for the cod in the North Atlantic. The proportion of the available items that are actually sampled is called the *sampling fraction*.

A parent population, often just called the *population*, is described in terms of its *parameters*, such as its mean, μ, and variance, σ^2. By convention Greek letters are used to denote these parameters.

A value derived from a sample is written in Roman letters: mean, $\bar{x}$, variance, s^2, etc. Such a number is the value of a *sample statistic* (or just *statistic*). When sample statistics are used to estimate the parent population parameters they are called *estimates*.

Thus if you take a random sample in which the mean is $\bar{x}$, you can use $\bar{x}$ to estimate the parent mean, μ. If in a particular sample $\bar{x} = 23.4$, then you can use 23.4 as an estimate of the population mean. The true value of μ will generally be somewhat different from your estimated value.

Upper case letters, X, Y, etc., are used to represent the random variables, and lower case letters, x, y, etc., to denote particular values of them. In the example of the Avonford voters, you could define X to be the percentage of voters, in a sample of size 30, showing support for Mrs Curtis. The particular value from this sample, $x = \left(\frac{12}{30}\right) \times 100 = 40\%$.

Sampling

There are essentially two reasons why you might wish to take a sample.

- To estimate the values of the parameters of the parent population.
- To conduct a hypothesis test.

There are many ways you can interpret data. First you will consider how sample data are collected and the steps you can take to ensure their quality.

An estimate of a parameter derived from sample data will in general differ from its true value. The difference is called the *sampling error*. To reduce the sampling error, you want your sample to be as representative of the parent population as you can make it. This, however, may be easier said than done.

Here are a number of questions that you should ask yourself when about to take a sample.

1 Are the data relevant?

It is a common mistake to replace what you need to measure by something else for which data are more easily obtained.

You must ensure that your data are relevant, giving values of whatever it is that you really want to measure. This was clearly not the case in the example of the *Avonford Star*, where the question people were asked, 'Who would make the best M.P.?', was not the one whose answer was required. The question should have been 'Which person do you intend to vote for?'.

2 Are the data likely to be biased?

Bias is a systematic error. If, for example, you wished to estimate the mean time of young women running 100 metres and did so by timing the members of a hockey team over that distance, your result would be biased. The hockey players would be fitter and more athletic than most young women and so your estimate for the time would be too low.

You must try to avoid bias in the selection of your sample.

3 Does the method of collection distort the data?

The process of collecting data must not interfere with the data. It is, for example, very easy when designing a questionnaire to frame questions in such a way as to lead people into making certain responses 'Are you a law-abiding citizen?' and 'Do you consider your driving to be above average?' are both questions inviting the answer 'Yes'.

In the case of collecting information on voting intentions another problem arises. Where people put the cross on their ballot papers is secret and so people are being asked to give away private information. There may well be those who find this offensive and react by deliberately giving false answers.

People often give the answer they think the questioner wants to receive.

4 Is the right person collecting the data?

Bias can be introduced by the choice of those taking the sample. For example, a school's authorities want to estimate the proportion of the students who smoke, which is against the school rules. Each form teacher is told to ask five students whether they smoke. Almost certainly some smokers will say 'No' to their teacher for fear of getting into trouble, even though they might say 'Yes' to a different person.

5 Is the sample large enough?

The sample must be sufficiently large for the results to have some meaning. In this case the intention was to look for differences of support between the four candidates and for that a sample of 30 is totally inadequate. For opinion polls, a sample size of about 1000 is common.

The sample size depends on the precision required in the results. For example, in the opinion polls for elections a much larger sample is required if you want the estimate to be reliable to within 1% than if 5% will do.

6 Is the sampling procedure appropriate in the circumstances?

The method of choosing the sample must be appropriate. Suppose, for example, that you were carrying out the survey for the *Avonford Star* of people's voting intentions in the forthcoming by-election. How would you select the sample of people you are going to ask?

If you stood in the town's high street in the middle of one morning and asked passers-by you would probably get an unduly high proportion of those who, for one reason or another, were not employed. It is quite possible that this group has different voting intentions from those in work.

If you selected names from the telephone directory, you would automatically exclude those who do not have telephones: the lower income groups, students and so on.

It is actually very difficult to come up with a plan which will yield a fair sample, one that is not biased in some direction or another. There are, however, a number of established sampling techniques and these are described in the next section of this chapter.

❓ Each of the situations below involves a *population* and a *sample*. In each case identify both, briefly but precisely.

1 An M.P. is interested in whether her constituents support proposed legislation to restore capital punishment for murder. Her staff report that letters on the proposed legislation have been received from 361 constituents of whom 309 support it.

2 A flour company wants to know what proportion of Manchester households bake some or all of their own bread. A sample of 500 residential addresses in Manchester is taken and interviewers are sent to these addresses. The interviewers are employed during regular working hours on weekdays and interview only during these hours.

3 The Chicago Police Department wants to know how black residents of Chicago feel about police service. A questionnaire with several questions about the

police is prepared. A sample of 300 postal addresses in predominantly black areas of Chicago is taken and a police officer is sent to each address to administer the questionnaire to an adult living there.

Each sampling situation contains a serious source of probable bias. In each case give the reason that bias may occur and also the direction of the bias.

[MEI]

Sampling techniques

In considering the following techniques it is worth repeating that a key aim when taking a sample is to obtain a sample that is *representative* of the parent population being investigated. It is assumed that the sampling is done without replacement, otherwise, for example, one person could give an opinion twice, or more. The fraction of the population which is selected is called the *sampling fraction*.

$$\text{Sampling fraction} = \frac{\text{sample size}}{\text{population size}}$$

Simple random sampling

In a *simple random sampling procedure*, every possible sample of a given size is equally likely to be selected. It follows that in such a procedure every member of the parent population is equally likely to be selected. However, the converse is not true. It is possible to devise a sampling procedure in which every member is equally likely to be selected but some samples are not permissible.

---

1 A school has 20 classes, each with 30 students. One student is chosen at random from each class, giving a sample size of 20. Why is this not a simple random sampling procedure?

2 If you write the name of each student in the school on a slip of paper, put all the slips in a box, shake it well and then take out 20, would this be a simple random sample?

Simple random sampling is fine when you can do it, but you must have a sampling frame. The selection of items within the frame is often done using tables of random numbers. Random numbers can be generated using a calculator or computer program.

Stratified sampling

You have already thought about the difficulty of conducting a survey of people's voting intentions in a particular area before an election. In that situation it is possible to identify a number of different sub-groups which you might expect to have different voting patterns: low, medium and high income groups; urban, suburban and rural dwellers; young, middle-aged and elderly voters; men and women; and so on. The sub-groups are called *strata*. In *stratified sampling*, you would ensure that all strata were sampled. You would need to sample from high income, suburban, elderly women; medium income, rural young men; etc. In this example, 54 strata ($3 \times 3 \times 3 \times 2$) have been identified. If the numbers sampled in the various strata are proportional to the size of their populations, the procedure is called *proportional stratified sampling*. If the sampling is not proportional, then appropriate weighting has to be used.

The selection of the items to be sampled within each stratum is usually done by simple random sampling. Stratified sampling will usually lead to more accurate results about the entire population, and will also give useful information about the individual strata.

Cluster sampling

Cluster sampling also starts with sub-groups, or strata, of the population, but in this case the items are chosen from one or several of the sub-groups. The sub-groups are now called clusters. It is important that each cluster should be reasonably representative of the entire population. If, for example, you were asked to investigate the incidence of a particular parasite in the puffin population of Northern Europe, it would be impossible to use simple random sampling. Rather you would select a number of sites and then catch some puffins at each place. This is cluster sampling. Instead of selecting from the whole population you are choosing from a limited number of clusters.

Systematic sampling

Systematic sampling is a method of choosing individuals from a sampling frame. If you were surveying telephone subscribers, you might select a number at random, say 66, and then sample the 66th name on every page of the directory. If the items in the sampling frame are numbered $1, 2, 3, \ldots$, you might choose a random starting point like 38 and then sample numbers 38, 138, 238 and so on.

When using systematic sampling you have to beware of any cyclic patterns within the frame. For example, a school list is made up form by form, each of exactly 25 children, in order of merit, so that numbers $1, 26, 51, 76, 101, \ldots$, in the frame are those at the top of their forms. If you sample every 50th child starting with number 26, you will conclude that the children in the school are very bright.

Quota sampling

Quota sampling is the method often used by companies employing people to carry out opinion surveys. An interviewer's quota is always specified in stratified terms, how many males and how many females, etc. The choice of who is sampled is then left up to the interviewer and so is definitely non-random.

Other sampling techniques

This is by no means a complete list of sampling techniques. *Survey design*, the formulation of the most appropriate sampling procedure in a particular situation, is a major topic within statistics.

EXERCISE 4A

1 (i) An accountant is sampling from a computer file. The first number is selected randomly and is item 47; the rest of the sample is selected automatically and comprises items 97, 147, 197, 247, 297,....

What type of sampling procedure is being used?

(ii) Pritam is a pupil at Avonford High School. He has been given a copy of the list of all students in the school. The list numbers the students from 1 to 2500.

Pritam generates a four-digit random number on his calculator, for example 0.4325. He multiplies the random number by 2500 and notes the integer part. For example, 0.4325×2500 results in 1081 so Pritam chooses the pupil listed as 1081. He repeats the process until he has a sample of 100 names.

(a) What type of sampling procedure is Pritam carrying out?
(b) What is the sampling fraction in this case?

(iii) Mr Jones wishes to find out if a mobile grocery service would be popular in Avonford. He chooses four streets at random in the town and calls at 15 randomly selected houses in each of the streets to seek the residents' views.
(a) What type of sampling procedure is he using?
(b) Is the procedure random?

(iv) Tracey is trying to encourage people to shop at her boutique. She has produced a short questionnaire and has employed four college students to administer it. The questionnaire asks people about their fashion preferences. Each student is told to question 20 women and 20 men and then to stop.
(a) What type of sampling procedure is Tracey using?
(b) Is the procedure random?
(c) Comment on the number of people that are surveyed.

2 (i) There are five year groups in the school Jane attends. She wishes to survey opinion about what to do with an unused section of field next to the playground. Because of a limited budget she has produced only 30 questionnaires.

There are 140 students in each of Years 1 and 2.
There are 100 students in each of Years 3 and 4.
There are 120 students in Year 5.

Jane plans to use a stratified sampling procedure.
(a) How many students from each year should Jane survey?
(b) What is the sampling fraction?

(ii) A factory safety inspector wishes to inspect a sample of vehicles to check for faulty tyres. The factory has 280 light vans, 21 company cars and 5 large-load vehicles.

The chairman has instructed that a sampling fraction of $\frac{1}{10}$ should be used and that each type of vehicle should be represented in the sample.
(a) How many of each vehicle type should be inspected?
(b) How should the inspector choose his sample? What is the sampling procedure called?

(iii) A small village has a population of 640. The population is classified by age as shown in the table below.

Age (years)	0–5	6–12	13–21	22–35	36–50	51+
Number of people	38	82	108	204	180	28

A survey of the inhabitants of the village is intended. A sample of size 80 is proposed.
(a) What is the overall sampling fraction?
(b) A stratified sample is planned. Calculate the approximate number that should be sampled from each age group.

3 Identify the sampling procedures that would be appropriate in the following situations.
(i) A local education officer wishes to estimate the mean number of children per family on a large housing estate.
(ii) A consumer protection body wishes to estimate the proportion of trains that are running late.
(iii) A marketing consultant wishes to investigate the proportion of households in a town that have a personal computer.
(iv) A local politician wishes to carry out a survey into people's views on capital punishment within your area.
(v) A health inspector wishes to investigate what proportion of people wear spectacles.

(vi) Ministry officials wish to estimate the proportion of cars with bald tyres.

(vii) A television company wishes to estimate the proportion of householders who have not paid their television licence fee.

(viii) The police want to find out how fast cars travel in the outside lane of a motorway.

(ix) A sociologist wants to know how many girlfriends the average 18-year-old boy has had.

(x) The headteacher of a large school wishes to estimate the average number of hours homework done per week by the students.

4 You have been given the job of refurnishing the college canteen. You wish to survey student opinion on this. You are considering a number of sampling methods. In each case describe the sampling method and list the advantages and disadvantages.

(i) Select every 25th student from the college's alphabetical listing of students.

(ii) Select students as they arrive at college, ensuring proportional numbers of males and females and from classes on different courses.

(iii) Select students as they enter the canteen.

(iv) Select students at random from first and second year-group listings and in proportion to the number on each list.

5 Sampling is required in the situations below. For each situation devise, name and describe a suitable strategy. (Your answer is expected to take about five to ten lines for each part.)

(i) A company producing strip lighting wishes to find an estimate of the life expectancy of a typical strip light. Suggest how they might obtain a suitable sample.

(ii) A tree surgeon wishes to estimate the number of damaged trees in a large forest. He has available a map of the forest. Suggest how he might select a sample.

(iii) A factory produces computer chips. It has five production lines. Each production line produces, on average, 100 000 chips per week. One week the quality control manager decides to take a random sample of 500 chips from each production line.

(a) Describe how she might arrange for a sample to be taken from a production line.

(b) What sampling method is she employing overall?

(iv) Avonford Technical College is anxious to monitor the use of the College car park, which has parking spaces for 100 cars. It is aware that the number of staff employed by the College is greater than this but also that some staff use public transport sometimes. It is considering giving staff a choice of a parking permit (cost as yet undecided) or paying for staff to use public transport.

How would you survey staff views on these proposals?

(v) Some of your fellow pupils have shown concern about the lack of available space to do private study. You have been asked to represent them in approaching the Principal in order to press for some improvement in appropriate study space. Before you do this you want to be sure that you are representing a majority view, not just the feelings of a few 'complaining' individuals.

Describe how you would survey the pupils to gain the required information.

Case study

SMOKING POLICY AT AVONFORD TERTIARY COLLEGE (ATC)

Avonford Tertiary College is located on five sites near the centre of Avonford. Each site specialises in a number of subjects or vocational areas.

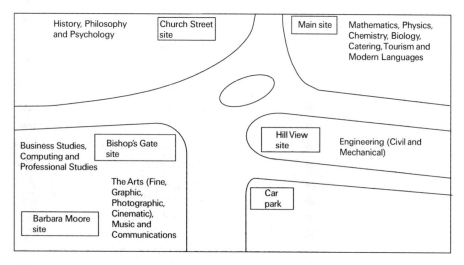

Figure 4.1

The student population is made up as shown in the table below.

	Full-time	Part-time
Male	1250	1000
Female	2750	500

Each student is based at one or other of the five sites.

Base site	Number of students
Main	2000
Church Street	500
Bishop's Gate	1000
Barbara Moore	800
Hill View	1200

The college has a policy relating to health matters. A section reads as follows:

Smoking

In the interests of promoting the well-being of staff, students and the general public, smoking is not permitted inside college buildings. Smoking is, however, allowed on the college grounds.

The issues relating to smoking have caused much debate around the college. The conversation recorded on page 123 was overheard in the canteen.

CHARLOTTE: It's dreadful coming through the main entrance in this place, all those smokers hanging around. I don't know why they do it.
I think smoking should be banned on college grounds. Everybody knows smoking's a mug's game. If you smoke you get lung cancer and all sorts of illnesses.

ASHOK: That's a load of nonsense. Smoking should be allowed inside the buildings. My dad smokes and he hasn't got lung cancer.
What's more, my grandad has smoked since he was 10 and he's 98 now so smoking can't be that bad.

Anyway I think it looks cool, a bit like that actor, what's his name ... Anyway, a ban would be discriminating against smokers.

SIÂN: I don't think we have enough information to make an informed comment.

Charlotte and Ashok stare at Siân for a moment, decide to ignore her and then carry on talking.

CHARLOTTE: My mum says that it's antisocial to smoke, especially in public places. She says it means other people are forced to smoke against their will. She called it *passive smoking*. Where she works they're not allowed to smoke. They've got a No Smoking Policy.

ASHOK: My dad says it's against civil liberties to prevent people smoking. Anyway, in the office where he works four out of the five people smoke, so that proves that the majority of people smoke.
And doctors smoke so it can't be that unhealthy.

SIÂN: The only way we can make statements about smoking is first to decide exactly what we want to know and then gather reliable evidence. I'm sure we could get this if we researched what is happening nationally or internationally. Also, it needs to be done properly. We might get relevant data on the internet. Wherever we get our information, though, we need to make sure we take a *representative sample*. Then we have to make policies which are fair to all people, even minority groups.

ASHOK: What about student views? It's most important that our views are heard. After all, it's us any decisions will affect.

CHARLOTTE: If I could find out the percentage of students at ATC who smoke and, for those that do smoke, how many cigarettes a day they smoke, then I could use the data to make a report to the college. They'd have to see sense and ban smoking.

ASHOK: I bet 80% of students smoke and that the average number of cigarettes they smoke per day is at least 20 cigarettes. It's not fair to prevent them from smoking. I'm going to collect data that show the college should provide indoor areas for smokers.

Charlotte and Ashok plan to collect data and use them to present a report to the College Management Committee.

In this case study you will carry out a number of tasks in order to gather relevant information about smoking.

You can

- either use data on Avonford Tertiary College to be found on the internet via www.mei.uk.com
- or gather data on your own school or college.

Your aim is to present a report to the Avonford Tertiary College Management Committee or the head of your own school or college.

TASK 1

Carry out some preliminary research into smoking related topics.

(i) Organise yourselves into groups of about four people.
(ii) As a group discuss the list of research topics below (you may add your own). Decide which topics you expect to provide the information that will best inform you about the pros and cons of smoking.
(iii) Discuss in your groups the best ways to gather information relating to the topics. These could include your school/college library, access to appropriate sites on the internet, interviewing experts such as doctors, tobacco company employees, newspaper shop owners/managers, etc.
(iv) Share the topics between your group and collect data in an appropriate form.
(v) In your groups, decide which findings are most useful and which are irrelevant. Present a summary of your findings as a group. This could involve a variety of approaches. For instance, you could use posters, a video recording of an interview, a debate between speakers holding opposite views, a written summary of your findings or you could present your findings on a flip chart with bullet points.

RESEARCH TOPICS
1 Smoking and health issues.

2 Arguments for and against smoking.
Civil liberties and smoking.
The organisation ASH.

3 Legal actions against tobacco companies.

4 Smoking policies in other communities: your school/college, national (shops, hospitals, transport, etc.), international (cities in the United States, other European countries, etc.).

5 Who smokes in the UK? (Age, gender, religion, etc.)

6 Tobacco is a drug. Should it be advertised at all?

Charlotte and Ashok have designed questionnaires to collect their data.

TASK 2

Write a short report commenting on the appropriateness of the questionnaires and suggesting any improvements.

CHARLOTTE'S QUESTIONNAIRE

Full-time ☐   Male   ☐
Part-time ☐   Female ☐

Site _____

Subject _____

Assume the following definitions:

Non-smoker: Somebody who currently never smokes.
Occasional smoker: Somebody who smokes but not every day.
Frequent smoker: Somebody who smokes every day.

Now answer the following questions.

1. Do you think that smokers should be banned from College   Yes ☐
   grounds?   No ☐

2. Which category do you fall into?   A. Non-smoker   ☐
                                           B. Occasional smoker ☐
                                           C. Frequent smoker   ☐

If you answered A you can now hand in your completed questionnaire.

If you answered B go to question 3.

If you answered C go to question 4

3. How many cigarettes do you smoke, typically, in *one week*?   5 or fewer ☐
                                                                 6–10   ☐
                                                                 11–15   ☐
                                                                 more, please state ☐

4. How many cigarettes do you smoke, typically, *per day*?   5 or fewer ☐
                                                                 6–10   ☐
                                                                 11–15   ☐
                                                                 more, please state ☐

ASHOK'S QUESTIONNAIRE

Full-time ☐   Male ☐
Part-time ☐   Female ☐

1. Everybody should have the right to smoke.   Agree ☐   Disagree ☐

2. Medical doctors are the people best qualified to make judgements about health.   Agree ☐   Disagree ☐

3. As some doctors smoke this indicates very strongly that smoking is not unhealthy.   Agree ☐   Disagree ☐

4. Lots of people have reported that they have smoked for many years without ill health. Consequently, smoking is not proved to be harmful.   Agree ☐   Disagree ☐

5. The College should provide indoor areas for students to smoke if they wish to.   Agree ☐   Disagree ☐

6. Do you smoke?   Yes ☐   No ☐

TASK 3

Charlotte and Ashok have to decide how to conduct their survey. In deciding how to do this they have to consider a number of *key issues*. Comment briefly on the key issues below.

KEY ISSUES

1 Is a sample necessary?

Given the questionnaires they plan to use:

2 Will the data be relevant?

3 Are the data likely to be biased?

4 Does the method of sampling or the person collecting the data distort the data?

TASK 4

Another key issue to be considered is whether the sampling procedure is appropriate in the circumstances. Explain how Charlotte or Ashok could collect a sample using each of the following methods.

(i)   Simple random sampling
(ii) Systematic sampling
(iii) Cluster sampling
(iv) Stratified sampling
(v)   Quota sampling

Explain which would be the most appropriate method.

TASK 5

Taking into account your answers to the previous tasks, carry out your survey. Use data from the Web site or collect data on your own school or college.

TASK 6

Write your report. Propose a policy on smoking, which may be a continuation of the present policy, and present arguments to support your proposal. Your arguments should be based on findings from your research and your survey.

KEY POINTS

1 There are essentially two reasons why you might wish to take a sample:

- to estimate the values of the parameters of the parent population
- to conduct a hypothesis test.

2 When taking a sample you should ensure that:

- the data are relevant
- the data are unbiased
- the data are not distorted by the act of collection
- a suitable person is collecting the data
- the sample is of a suitable size
- a suitable sampling procedure is being followed.

3 Some sampling procedures are:

- simple random sampling
- stratified sampling
- cluster sampling
- systematic sampling
- quota sampling.

Further probability

An estate had seven houses;
Each house had seven cats;
Each cat ate seven mice;
Each mouse ate seven grains of wheat.
Wheat grains, mice, cats and houses,
How many were there on the estate?

Ancient Egyptian problem

THE AVONFORD STAR

Child Prodigy

Little Gary Forest looks like any other toddler but all the evidence points to him being a budding genius.

Recently Gary's mother gave him five bricks to play with, each showing one of the numbers **1**, **2**, **3**, **4** and **5**. Without hesitation Gary sat down and placed them in the correct order.

Little Gary Forest looks like being a budding genius!

What is the probability that Gary chose the bricks at random and just happened by chance to get them in the right order?

There are two ways of looking at the situation. You can think of Gary selecting the five bricks as five events, one after another. Alternatively, you can think of 1, 2, 3, 4, 5 as one outcome out of several possible outcomes and work out the probability that way.

FIVE EVENTS

Look at the diagram.

| 1 | | 2 | | 3 | | 4 | | 5 |

Figure 5.1

If Gary had actually chosen them at random:

the probability of first selecting **1** is $\frac{1}{5}$

the probability of next selecting **2** is $\frac{1}{4}$ ← 1 correct choice from 4 remaining bricks

the probability of next selecting **3** is $\frac{1}{3}$

the probability of next selecting **4** is $\frac{1}{2}$

then only **5** remains so the probability of selecting it is 1

So the probability of getting the correct numerical sequence at random is

$$\frac{1}{5} \times \frac{1}{4} \times \frac{1}{3} \times \frac{1}{2} \times 1 = \frac{1}{120}$$

OUTCOMES

How many ways are there of putting five bricks in a line?

To start with there are five bricks to choose from, so there are five ways of choosing brick 1. Then there are four bricks left and so there are four ways of choosing brick 2. And so on.

The total number of ways is

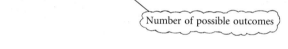

5	×	4	×	3	×	2	×	1	= 120
Brick 1		Brick 2		Brick 3		Brick 4		Brick 5	

Only one of these is the order 1, 2, 3, 4, 5, so the probability of Gary selecting it at random is $\frac{1}{120}$.

Number of possible outcomes

❓ Do you agree with the *Avonford Star* that Gary is a child prodigy, or do you think it was just by chance that he put the bricks down in the right order?

What further information would you want to be convinced that he is a budding genius?

Factorials

In the last example you saw that the number of ways of placing five different bricks in a line is $5 \times 4 \times 3 \times 2 \times 1$. This number is called 5 *factorial* and is written 5!. You will often meet expressions of this form.

In general the number of ways of placing n different objects in a line is $n!$, where $n! = n \times (n-1) \times (n-2) \times \cdots \times 3 \times 2 \times 1$.

n must be a positive integer

EXAMPLE 5.1

Calculate 7!

SOLUTION

$$7! = 7 \times 6 \times 5 \times 4 \times 3 \times 2 \times 1 = 5040$$

Some typical relationships between factorial numbers are illustrated below:

$10! = 10 \times 9!$ or in general $n! = n \times [(n-1)!]$

$10! = 10 \times 9 \times 8 \times 7!$ or in general $n! = n \times (n-1) \times (n-2) \times [(n-3)!]$

These are useful when simplifying expressions involving factorials.

EXAMPLE 5.2

Calculate $\dfrac{5!}{3!}$

SOLUTION

$$\frac{5!}{3!} = \frac{5 \times 4 \times 3!}{3!} = 5 \times 4 = 20$$

EXAMPLE 5.3

Calculate $\dfrac{7! \times 5!}{3! \times 4!}$

SOLUTION

$$\frac{7! \times 5!}{3! \times 4!} = \frac{7 \times 6 \times 5 \times 4 \times 3! \times 5 \times 4!}{3! \times 4!} = 7 \times 6 \times 5 \times 4 \times 5 = 4200$$

EXAMPLE 5.4

Write $37 \times 36 \times 35$ in terms of factorials only.

SOLUTION

$$37 \times 36 \times 35 = \frac{37 \times 36 \times 35 \times 34!}{34!} = \frac{37!}{34!}$$

1 Calculate **(i)** $8!$ **(ii)** $\dfrac{8!}{6!}$ **(iii)** $\dfrac{5! \times 6!}{7! \times 4!}$

2 Simplify **(i)** $\dfrac{(n-1)!}{n!}$ **(ii)** $\dfrac{(n-1)!}{(n-2)!}$

3 Simplify **(i)** $\dfrac{(n+3)!}{(n+1)!}$ **(ii)** $\dfrac{n!}{(n-2)!}$

4 Write in factorial notation

(i) $\dfrac{8 \times 7 \times 6}{5 \times 4 \times 3}$ **(ii)** $\dfrac{15 \times 16}{4 \times 3 \times 2}$ **(iii)** $\dfrac{(n+1)n(n-1)}{4 \times 3 \times 2}$

5 Factorise **(i)** $7! + 8!$ **(ii)** $n! + (n+1)!$

6 How many different four letter words can be formed from the letters A, B, C, D if letters cannot be repeated? (The words do not need to mean anything.)

7 How many different ways can eight books be arranged in a row on a shelf?

8 In a greyhound race there are six runners. How many different ways are there for the six dogs to finish?

9 In a 60-metre hurdles race there are five runners, one from each of the nations Austria, Belgium, Canada, Denmark and England.
(i) How many different finishing orders are there?
(ii) What is the probability of predicting the finishing order by choosing first, second, third, fourth and fifth at random?

10 John has a CD player which can play CDs in 'shuffle' mode. If a CD is played in 'shuffle' mode the tracks are selected in a random order with a different track selected each time until all the tracks have been played.

John plays a 14-track CD in 'shuffle' mode.
(i) In how many different orders could the tracks be played?
(ii) What is the probability that 'shuffle' mode will play the tracks in the normal set order listed on the CD?

11 In a 'Goal of the season' competition, participants pay an entry fee of ten pence. They are then asked to rank ten goals in order of quality.

The organisers select their 'correct' order at random. They offer £100 000 to anybody who matches their order. There are no other prizes.
(i) What is the probability of a participant's order being the same as that of the organisers?
(ii) How much does a participant expect to win or lose with each entry?
(iii) Five million people enter the competition. How much profit do the organisers expect to make?

12 The letters O, P, S and T are placed in a line at random. What is the probability that they form a word in the English language?

1 Solve the inequality $n! > 10^m$ for each of the cases $m = 3, 4, 5$.

2 In how many ways can you write 42 using factorials only?

3 (i) There are 4! ways of placing the four letters S, T, A, R in a line, if each of them must appear exactly once. How many ways are there if each letter may appear any number of times (i.e. between 0 and 4)? Formulate a general rule.

(ii) There are 4! ways of placing the letters S, T, A, R in line. How many ways are there of placing in line the letters
(a) S, T, A, A   (b) S, T, T, T?
Formulate a general rule for dealing with repeated letters.

Permutations

THE AVONFORD STAR

Beginner's Luck for Joyeeta

It was Joyeeta Ganguly's first ever visit to the racecourse and she left staggering under the weight of her winnings.

It all happened on the 3.15, a 16-horse race, when Joyeeta picked the first, second and third placed horses for a special 500-1 bet.

'I just chose the horses with pretty names' said Joyeeta.

What is the probability of Joyeeta's result?

The winner can be chosen in 16 ways.
The second horse can be chosen in 15 ways.
The third horse can be chosen in 14 ways.

Thus the total number of ways of placing three horses in the first three positions is $16 \times 15 \times 14 = 3360$. So the probability that Joyeeta's random selection is correct is $\frac{1}{3360}$.

In this example attention is given to the order in which the horses finish. The solution required a *permutation* of three objects from sixteen.

In general the number of permutations, ^nP_r, of r objects from n is given by
$$^nP_r = n \times (n-1) \times (n-2) \times \cdots \times (n-r+1).$$

This can be written more compactly as

$$^nP_r = \frac{n!}{(n-r)!}$$

Combinations

It is often the case that you are not concerned with the order in which items are chosen, only with which ones are picked.

To take part in the National Lottery you fill in a ticket by selecting 6 numbers out of a possible 49 (numbers 1, 2, ..., 49). When the draw is made a machine selects six numbers at random. If they are the same as the six on your ticket, you win the jackpot.

❓ You have the six winning numbers. Does it matter in which order the machine picked them?

The probability of a single ticket winning the jackpot is often said to be 1 in 14 million. How can you work out this figure?

The key question is, how many ways are there of choosing 6 numbers out of 49?

If the order mattered, the answer would be $^{49}P_6$, or $49 \times 48 \times 47 \times 46 \times 45 \times 44$.

However, the order does not matter. 1, 3, 15, 19, 31 and 48 is the same as 15, 48, 31, 1, 19, 3 and 3, 19, 48, 1, 15, 31 and lots more. For each set of six numbers there are 6! arrangements that all count as being the same.

So, the number of ways of selecting six balls, given that the order does not matter, is $\dfrac{49 \times 48 \times 47 \times 46 \times 45 \times 44}{6!}$.

This is $\dfrac{^{49}P_6}{6!}$

This is called the number of *combinations* of 6 objects from 49 and is denoted by $^{49}C_6$.

❓ Show that $^{49}C_6$ can be written as $\dfrac{49!}{6!\,43!}$

Returning to the National Lottery, it follows that the probability of your one ticket winning the jackpot is $\dfrac{1}{^{49}C_6}$.

❓ Check that this is about 1 in 14 million.

This example shows a general result, that the number of ways of selecting r objects from n, when the order does not matter, is given by

$$^nC_r = \frac{n!}{r!(n-r)!} = \frac{^nP_r}{r!}$$

? How can you prove this general result?

Another notation for ^nC_r is $\binom{n}{r}$.

! The notation $\binom{n}{r}$ looks exactly like a column vector and so there is the possibility of confusing the two. However, the context should usually make the meaning clear.

EXAMPLE 5.5

A School Governors' committee of five people is to be chosen from eight applicants. How many different selections are possible?

SOLUTION

Number of selections $= {}^8C_5 = \dfrac{8!}{5!3!} = \dfrac{8 \times 7 \times 6}{3 \times 2 \times 1} = 56.$

EXAMPLE 5.6

In how many ways can a committee of four people be selected from four applicants?

SOLUTION

Common sense tells us that there is only one way to make the committee, that is by appointing all applicants. However, if we work from the formula

$$^4C_4 = \frac{4!}{4! \times 0!} = \frac{1}{0!} \text{ and this must } = 1$$

To achieve the answer 1 requires the convention that $0!$ is taken to be 1.

? Use the convention $0! = 1$ to show that $^nC_0 = {}^nC_n = 1$ for all values of n.

The binomial coefficients, ^nC_r

In the last section you met numbers of the form ^nC_r. These are called the binomial coefficients; the reason for this is explained in the appendix on page 176 and in the next chapter.

ACTIVITY

Use the formula $^nC_r = \dfrac{n!}{r!(n-r)!}$ and the results $\binom{n}{0} = \binom{n}{n} = 1$ to check that the entries in this table, for $n = 6$ and 7, are correct.

r	0	1	2	3	4	5	6	7
$n=6$	1	6	15	20	15	6	1	
$n=7$	1	7	21	35	35	21	7	1

It is very common to present values of ^nC_r in a table shaped like an isosceles triangle, known as Pascal's triangle.

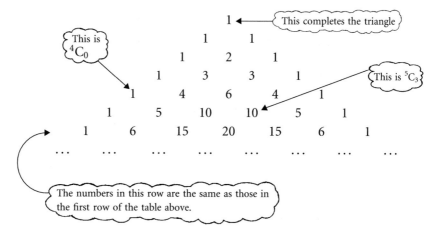

Pascal's triangle makes it easy to see two important properties of binomial coefficients:

1 SYMMETRY: $^nC_r = {}^nC_{n-r}$

If you are choosing 11 players from a pool of 15 possible players you can either name the 11 you have selected or name the 4 you have rejected. Similarly, every choice of r objects included in a selection from n distinct objects corresponds to a choice of $(n-r)$ objects which are excluded. Therefore $^nC_r = {}^nC_{n-r}$.

This provides a short cut in calculations when r is large. For example

$$^{100}C_{96} = {}^{100}C_4 = \frac{100 \times 99 \times 98 \times 97}{1 \times 2 \times 3 \times 4} = 3\,921\,225.$$

It also shows that the list of values of ^nC_r for any particular value of n is unchanged by being reversed. For example, when $n = 6$ the list is the seven numbers 1, 6, 15, 20, 15, 6, 1.

2 ADDITION: $^{n+1}C_{r+1} = {}^nC_r + {}^nC_{r+1}$

Look at the entry 15 in the bottom row of Pascal's triangle, towards the right. The two entries above and either side of it are 10 and 5,

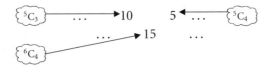

and $15 = 10 + 5$. In this case $^6C_4 = {}^5C_3 + {}^5C_4$. This is an example of the general result that $^{n+1}C_{r+1} = {}^nC_r + {}^nC_{r+1}$. Check that all the entries in Pascal's triangle (except the 1s) are found in this way.

This can be used to build up a table of values of ^nC_r without much calculation. If you know all the values of ^nC_r for any particular value of n you can add pairs of values to obtain all the values of $^{n+1}C_r$, i.e. the next row, except the first and last, which always equal 1.

Why is this so? Suppose you are choosing $r + 1$ objects from $n + 1$ distinct objects. You can do this in $^{n+1}C_{r+1}$ ways. Now give any one particular object a label, X say. The selections now split into two categories, those which contain X and those which do not. If X is included you have to choose r more objects from the other n objects; this can be done in ^nC_r ways. If X is not included you have to choose all $r + 1$ objects from the other n objects; this can be done in $^nC_{r+1}$ ways. Between them these two cases cover all the possibilities, and therefore $^{n+1}C_{r+1} = {}^nC_r + {}^nC_{r+1}$.

 How can you prove $^{n+1}C_{r+1} = {}^nC_r + {}^nC_{r+1}$ using algebra?

Calculating probabilities in less simple cases

EXAMPLE 5.7

A committee of 5 is to be chosen from a list of 14 people, 6 of whom are men and 8 women. Their names are to be put in a hat and then 5 drawn out.

What is the probability that this procedure produces a committee with no women?

SOLUTION

The probability of an all-male committee of five people is given by

$$\frac{\text{The number of ways of choosing 5 people out of 6}}{\text{The number of ways of choosing 5 people out of 14}}$$

There are 6 men

There are 14 people

$$= \frac{^6C_5}{^{14}C_5} = \frac{6}{2002} \approx 0.003.$$

THE AVONFORD STAR
Where will the bus go?

John Crawler, Operations Director for Avonford Transport, has announced that the public will be consulted about the exact route of the new bus service due to start in April. Mr Crawler said 'The new route will run from Avonford to Chandford via Brantwood and will be extended to Digby when new buses arrive in September. As local people know, there are several roads connecting these towns, so we need to find out from our future passengers which one of the many possible routes will be the most useful.'

Local resident Agnes Philpott is not happy. 'The chances of their getting the route that suits me are less than one in a hundred' she complained.

Is Agnes right? How many routes are there from Avonford to Digby? Start by looking at the first two legs, Avonford to Brantwood and Brantwood to Chandford.

There are three roads from Avonford to Brantwood and two roads from Brantwood to Chandford. How many routes are there from Avonford to Chandford passing through Brantwood on the way?

Look at figure 5.2.

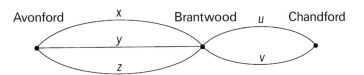

Figure 5.2

The answer is $3 \times 2 = 6$ because there are three ways of doing the first leg, followed by two for the second leg. The six routes are

$$x - u \qquad y - u \qquad z - u$$
$$x - v \qquad y - v \qquad z - v$$

There are also four roads from Chandford to Digby. So each of the six routes from Avonford to Chandford has four possible ways of going on to Digby. There are now $6 \times 4 = 24$ routes. See figure 5.3.

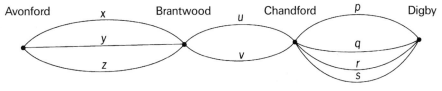

Figure 5.3

They can be listed systematically as follows:

$x-u-p$	$y-u-p$	$z-u-p$	$x-v-p$	$y-v-p$	$z-v-p$
$x-u-q$	....	....	....	....	....
$x-u-r$	....	....	....	....	....
$x-u-s$	....	....	....	....	$z-v-s$

In general, if there are a outcomes from experiment A, b outcomes from experiment B and c outcomes from experiment C then there are $a \times b \times c$ different possible combined outcomes from the three experiments.

1 If Avonford Transport chooses its route at random, what is the probability that it will be the one Agnes Philpott wants?
Is her comment in the newspaper justified?

2 In this example the probability was worked out by finding the number of possible routes. How else could it have been worked out?

EXAMPLE 5.8

A cricket team consisting of 6 batsmen, 4 bowlers and 1 wicket-keeper is to be selected from a group of 18 cricketers comprising 9 batsmen, 7 bowlers and 2 wicket-keepers. How many different teams can be selected?

SOLUTION

The batsmen can be selected in $^9C_6$ ways.
The bowlers can be selected in $^7C_4$ ways.
The wicket-keepers can be selected in $^2C_1$ ways.
Therefore total number of teams $= {}^9C_6 \times {}^7C_4 \times {}^2C_1$

$$= \frac{9!}{3!\,6!} \times \frac{7!}{3!\,4!} \times \frac{2!}{1!\,1!}$$

$$= \frac{9 \times 8 \times 7}{3 \times 2 \times 1} \times \frac{7 \times 6 \times 5}{3 \times 2 \times 1} \times 2$$

$$= 5880 \text{ ways.}$$

EXERCISE 5B

1 (i) Find the values of **(a)** $^6P_2$ **(b)** $^8P_4$ **(c)** $^{10}P_4$
(ii) Find the values of **(a)** $^6C_2$ **(b)** $^8C_4$ **(c)** $^{10}C_4$
(iii) Show that, for the values of n and r in parts (i) and (ii),

$$^nC_r = \frac{^nP_r}{r!}$$

2 There are 15 runners in a horse race. What is the probability of correctly guessing the first three finishers in their finishing order?

3 To win the jackpot in a lottery a contestant must correctly select six numbers from the numbers 1 to 30 inclusive. What is the probability that a contestant wins the jackpot with one selection of six numbers?

4 A group of 5 computer programmers is to be chosen to form the night shift from a set of 14 programmers. In how many ways can the programmers be chosen if the 5 chosen must include the shift-leader who is one of the 14?

5 My brother Mark decides to put together a rock band from amongst his year at school. He wants a lead singer, a guitarist, a keyboard player and a drummer. He invites applications and gets 7 singers, 5 guitarists, 4 keyboard players and 2 drummers. Assuming each person applies only once, in how many ways can Mark put the group together?

6 A touring party of hockey players is made up of 5 players from each of England, Ireland and Scotland, and 3 from Wales.
(i) How many different selections of 11 players can be made for a team?
(ii) In one match, it is decided to have 3 players from each of England, Ireland and Scotland and 2 from Wales. How many different team selections can now be made?

7 A committee of four is to be selected from ten candidates, six men and four women.
(i) In how many distinct ways can the committee be chosen?
(ii) Assuming that each candidate is equally likely to be selected, determine the probabilities that the chosen committee contains
  (a) no women
  (b) two men and two women.

8 A factory advertises for four employees. Eight men and five women apply.
(i) How many different selections of employees are possible from these applicants?
(ii) How many of these selections include no men?
(iii) What is the probability that only women applicants are successful?
(iv) What assumption did you make in part (iii)?

9 A committee of four is to be selected from five boys and four girls. The members are selected at random.
(i) How many different selections are possible?
(ii) What is the probability that the committee will be made up of
  (a) all girls?
  (b) more boys than girls?

10 Baby Imran has a set of alphabet blocks. His mother often uses the blocks I, M, R, A and N to spell Imran's name.

(i) One day she leaves him playing with these five blocks. When she comes back into the room Imran has placed them in the correct order to spell his name. What is the probability of Imran placing the blocks in this order? (He is only 18 months old so he certainly cannot spell!)

(ii) A couple of days later she leaves Imran playing with all 26 of the alphabet blocks. When she comes back into the room she again sees that he has placed the five blocks I, M, R, A and N in the correct order to spell his name. What is the probability of him choosing the five correct blocks and placing them in this order?

11 At a small branch of the MidWest bank the manager has a staff of 12, consisting of 5 men and 7 women including a Mr Brown and a Mrs Green. The manager receives a letter from head office saying that 4 of his staff are to be made redundant. In the interests of fairness the manager selects the 4 staff at random.

(i) How many different selections are possible?

(ii) How many of these selections include both Mr Brown and Mrs Green?

(iii) Write down the probability that both Mr Brown and Mrs Green will be made redundant.

Before the redundancies are announced, a further letter arrives from head office saying that, in accordance with the company's equal opportunities policy, two men and two women must be made redundant. The manager scraps the original redundancy list and now chooses two men at random and two women at random.

(iv) How many different selections are possible now?

(v) Find the probability that both Mr Brown and Mrs Green are made redundant now.

12 *Alpha Bet* is a weekly lottery in which a selection of five *different* letters, chosen at random from the 26 letters A to Z inclusive, appear on each ticket. Each ticket has a different combination of letters printed on it. At the end of a week, five winning letters are chosen. Each person buying a ticket for the lottery pays £1.

Prizes are awarded depending on the number of letters on the ticket which match with the winning letters. For example, when the winning letters are D, G, K, M, X, a ticket with the letters E, K, M, R, X has three matching letters. The order of the letters on a ticket does not matter nor does the order in which they are drawn.

The values of prizes are given in the table below.

Number of matching letters	3	4	5
Prize	£10	£100	£1000

(i) What is the largest number of tickets that could be sold in a week?

Consider a week when all possible tickets are sold.

(ii) What is the probability that I win the £1000 prize if I buy only one ticket?

(iii) If the winning letters are D, G, K, M, X, give *two* examples of different tickets which would win a prize of £100. Show that altogether there are 105 tickets which would win a prize of £100.

(iv) Find the number of tickets that would win a prize of £10.

(v) Show that the chance of a ticket winning a prize is roughly 1 in 30.

(vi) Show that about half the stake money is returned in prizes.

KEY POINTS

1 The number of ways of arranging n unlike objects in a line is $n!$

2 $n! = n \times (n-1) \times (n-2) \times (n-3) \times \cdots \times 3 \times 2 \times 1.$

3 The number of *permutations* of r objects from n is

$$^{n}P_{r} = \frac{n!}{(n-r)!}$$

4 The number of *combinations* of r objects from n is

$$^{n}C_{r} = \frac{n!}{(n-r)!\,r!}$$

5 For permutations the order matters. For combinations it does not.

6 By convention $0! = 1$.

6 The binomial distribution

To be or not to be, that is the question.

Shakespeare (Hamlet)

THE AVONFORD STAR

Samantha's great invention

Mother of three, Samantha Weeks, has done more than her bit to protect the environment. She has invented the first cheap energy-saving light bulb.

Now Samantha is out to prove that she is not only a clever scientist but a smart business woman as well. For Samantha is setting up her own factory to make and sell her SUPERSAVER bulbs.

Samantha admits there are still some technical problems . . .

Samantha Weeks hopes to make a big success of her light industry

Samantha's production process is indeed not very good and there is a probability of 0.1 that any bulb will be substandard and so not last as long as it should.

She decides to sell her bulbs in packs of three and believes that if one bulb in a pack is substandard the customers will not complain but that if two or more are substandard they will do so. She also believes that complaints should be kept down to no more than 2.5% of customers. Does she meet her target?

Imagine a pack of Samantha's bulbs. There are eight different ways that good (G) and substandard (S) bulbs can be arranged in Samantha's packs, each with its associated probability.

Arrangement			Probability	Good	Substandard
G	G	G	$0.9 \times 0.9 \times 0.9 = 0.729$	3	0
G	G	S	$0.9 \times 0.9 \times 0.1 = 0.081$	2	1
G	S	G	$0.9 \times 0.1 \times 0.9 = 0.081$	2	1
S	G	G	$0.1 \times 0.9 \times 0.9 = 0.081$	2	1
G	S	S	$0.9 \times 0.1 \times 0.1 = 0.009$	1	2
S	G	S	$0.1 \times 0.9 \times 0.1 = 0.009$	1	2
S	S	G	$0.1 \times 0.1 \times 0.9 = 0.009$	1	2
S	S	S	$0.1 \times 0.1 \times 0.1 = 0.001$	0	3

Putting these results together gives this table:

Good	Substandard	Probability
3	0	0.729
2	1	0.243
1	2	0.027
0	3	0.001

So the probability of more than one substandard bulb in a pack is

$$0.027 + 0.001 = 0.028 \text{ or } 2.8\%$$

This is slightly more than the 2.5% that Samantha regards as acceptable.

What business advice would you give Samantha?

In this example we wrote down all the possible outcomes and found their probabilities one at a time, as you do in a tree diagram. Even with just three bulbs this was repetitive. If Samantha had packed her bulbs in boxes of six it would have taken 64 lines to list them all. Clearly we need to find a less cumbersome approach.

You will have noticed that in the case of two good bulbs and one substandard, the probability is the same for each of the three arrangements in the box.

Arrangement	Probability	Good	Substandard
G G S	$0.9 \times 0.9 \times 0.1 = 0.081$	2	1
G S G	$0.9 \times 0.1 \times 0.9 = 0.081$	2	1
S G G	$0.1 \times 0.9 \times 0.9 = 0.081$	2	1

So the probability of this outcome is $3 \times 0.081 = 0.243$. The number 3 arises because there are three ways of arranging two good and one substandard bulb in the box. This is a result you have already met in the previous chapter but written slightly differently.

EXAMPLE 6.1

How many different ways are there of arranging the letters *GGS*?

SOLUTION

Since all the letters are either *G* or *S*, all you need to do is to count the number of ways of choosing the letter *G* two times out of three letters. This is

$$^{3}C_{2} = \frac{3!}{2! \times 1!} = \frac{6}{2} = 3$$

So what does this tell you? There was no need to list all the possibilities for Samantha's boxes of bulbs. The information could have been written down like this:

Good	Substandard	Expression	Probability
3	0	$^3C_3\,(0.9)^3$	0.729
2	1	$^3C_2\,(0.9)^2(0.1)^1$	0.243
1	2	$^3C_1\,(0.9)^1(0.1)^2$	0.027
0	3	$^3C_0\,(0.1)^3$	0.001

The binomial distribution

Samantha's light bulbs are an example of a common type of situation which is modelled by the binomial distribution. In describing such situations in this book, we emphasise the fact by using the word trial rather than the more general term experiment.

- You are conducting trials on random samples of a certain size, denoted by n.
- There are just two possible outcomes (in this case substandard and good). These are often referred to as *success* and *failure*.
- Both outcomes have fixed probabilities, the two adding to 1. The probability of success is usually called p, that of failure q, so $p + q = 1$.
- The probability of success in any trial is independent of the outcomes of previous trials.

You can then list the probabilities of the different possible outcomes as in the table above.

The method of the previous section can be applied more generally. You can call the probability of a substandard bulb p (instead of 0.1), the probability of a good bulb q (instead of 0.9) and the number of substandard bulbs in a packet of three, X.

Then the possible values of X and their probabilities are as shown in the table below.

X	0	1	2	3
Probability	q^3	$3pq^2$	$3p^2q$	p^3

This package of values of X with their associated probabilities is called a *probability distribution*.

If Samantha decided to put five bulbs in a packet the probability distribution would be

X	0	1	2	3	4	5
Probability	q^5	$5pq^4$	$10p^2q^3$	$10p^3q^2$	$5p^4q$	p^5

{ 10 is $^5C_2$ }

The entry for $X = 2$, for example, arises because there are two 'successes' (substandard bulbs), giving probability p^2, and three 'failures' (good bulbs), giving probability q^3, and these can happen in $^5C_2 = 10$ ways. This can be written as $P(X = 2) = 10p^2q^3$.

If you are already familiar with the binomial theorem, you will notice that the probabilities in the table are the terms of the binomial expansion of $(q + p)^5$. This is why this is called a binomial distribution. Notice also that the sum of these probabilities is $(q + p)^5 = 1^5 = 1$, since $q + p = 1$, which is to be expected since the distribution covers all possible outcomes.

Note

The binomial theorem on the expansion of powers such as $(q + p)^n$ is covered in *Pure Mathematics 1*. The essential points are given in the appendix on page 176.

The general case

The general binomial distribution deals with the possible numbers of successes when there are n trials, each of which may be a success (with probability p) or a failure (with probability q); p and q are fixed positive numbers and $p + q = 1$. This distribution is denoted by $B(n, p)$. So, the original probability distribution for the number of substandard bulbs in Samantha's boxes of three is $B(3, 0.1)$.

For $B(n, p)$, the probability of r successes in n trials is found by the same argument as before. Each success has probability p and each failure has probability q, so the probability of r successes and $(n - r)$ failures in a particular order is $p^r q^{n-r}$. The positions in the sequence of n trials which the successes occupy can be chosen in ^nC_r ways. Therefore

$$P(X = r) = {}^nC_r p^r q^{n-r} \quad \text{for } 0 \leqslant r \leqslant n$$

The successive probabilities for $X = 0, 1, 2, \ldots, n$ are the terms of the binomial expansion of $(q + p)^n$.

Notes

1 The number of successes, X, is a variable which takes a restricted set of values ($X = 0, 1, 2, \ldots, n$) each of which has a known probability of occurring. This is an example of a *random variable*. Random variables are usually denoted by upper case letters, such as X, but the particular values they may take are written in lower case, such as r. To state that X has the binomial distribution $B(n, p)$ you can use the abbreviation $X \sim B(n, p)$, where the symbol $\sim$ means 'has the distribution'.

2 It is often the case that you use a theoretical distribution, such as the binomial, to describe a random variable that occurs in real life. This process is called modelling and it enables you to carry out relevant calculations. If the theoretical distribution matches the real life variable perfectly, then the model is perfect. Usually, however, the match is quite good but not perfect. In this case the results of any calculations will not necessarily give a completely accurate description of the real life situation. They may, nonetheless, be very useful.

1 The recovery ward in a maternity hospital has six beds. What is the probability that the mothers there have between them four girls and two boys? (You may assume that there are no twins and that a baby is equally likely to be a girl or a boy.)

2 A typist has a probability of 0.99 of typing a letter correctly. He makes his mistakes at random. He types a sentence containing 200 letters. What is the probability that he makes exactly one mistake?

3 In a well-known game you have to decide which your opponent is going to choose: 'Paper', 'Stone' or 'Scissors'. If you guess entirely at random, what is the probability that you are right exactly 5 times out of 15?

4 There is a fault in a machine making microchips, with the result that only 80% of those it produces work. A random sample of eight microchips made by this machine is taken. What is the probability that exactly six of them work?

5 An airport is situated in a place where poor visibility (less than 800 m) can be expected 25% of the time. A pilot flies into the airport on ten different occasions.
   (i) What is the probability that he encounters poor visibility exactly four times?
   (ii) What other factors could influence the probability?

6 Three coins are tossed.
   (i) What is the probability of all three showing heads?
   (ii) What is the probability of two heads and one tail?
   (iii) What is the probability of one head and two tails?
   (iv) What is the probability of all three showing tails?
   (v) Show that the probabilities for the four possible outcomes add up to 1.

7 A coin is tossed ten times.
   (i) What is the probability of it coming down heads five times and tails five times?
   (ii) Which is more likely: exactly seven heads or more than seven heads?

8 In an election 30% of people support the Progressive Party. A random sample of eight voters is taken.
 (i) What is the probability that it contains
   (a) 0 (b) 1 (c) 2 (d) at least 3 supporters of the Progressive Party?
 (ii) Which is the most likely number of Progressive Party supporters to find in a sample of size eight?

9 There are 15 children in a class.
 (i) What is the probability that
   (a) 0 (b) 1 (c) 2 (d) at least 3 were born in January?
 (ii) What assumption have you made in answering this question? How valid is this assumption in your view?

10 Criticise this argument.
 If you toss two coins they can come down three ways: two heads, one head and one tail, or two tails. There are three outcomes and so each of them must have probability one third.

The expectation of B(n, p)

EXAMPLE 6.2

The number of substandard bulbs in a packet of three of Samantha's bulbs is modelled by the random variable X. $X \sim B(3, 0.1)$.
(i) Find the expected frequencies of obtaining 0, 1, 2 and 3 substandard bulbs in 2000 packets.
(ii) Find the mean number of substandard bulbs per packet.

SOLUTION

(i) $P(X = 0) = 0.729$ (as on page 143), so the expected frequency of packets with no substandard bulbs is $2000 \times 0.729 = 1458$.

Similarly, the other expected frequencies are
 for 1 substandard bulb: $2000 \times 0.243 = 486$
 for 2 substandard bulbs: $2000 \times 0.027 = 54$
 for 3 substandard bulbs: $2000 \times 0.001 = 2$.

Check:
$1458 + 486 + 54 + 2$
$= 2000$

(ii) The expected total of substandard bulbs in 2000 packets is

$$0 \times 1458 + 1 \times 486 + 2 \times 54 + 3 \times 2 = 600.$$

Therefore the mean number of substandard bulbs per packet is $\frac{600}{2000} = 0.3$.

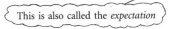

This is also called the *expectation*

Notice in this example that to calculate the mean we have multiplied each probability by 2000 to get the frequency, multiplied each frequency by the number of faulty bulbs, added these numbers together and finally divided by

2000. Of course we could have obtained the mean with less calculation by just multiplying each number of faulty bulbs by its probability and then summing, i.e. by finding $\sum_{r=0}^{3} r \times P(X = r)$. This is the standard method for finding an expectation, as you saw on page 85.

Notice also that the mean or expectation of X is $0.3 = 3 \times 0.1 = np$. The result for the general binomial distribution is the same:

if $X \sim B(n, p)$ then the expectation of X is np.

This seems obvious: if the probability of success in each single trial is p, then the expected numbers of successes in n independent trials is np. However, since what seems obvious is not always true, a proper proof is required.

Let us take the case when $n = 5$. The distribution table for $B(5, p)$ is as on page 145, and expectation of X

$$
\begin{aligned}
&= 0 \times q^5 + 1 \times 5pq^4 + 2 \times 10p^2q^3 + 3 \times 10p^3q^2 \\
&\quad + 4 \times 5p^4q + 5 \times p^5 \\
&= 5pq^4 + 20p^2q^3 + 30p^3q^2 + 20p^4q + 5p^5 \\
&= 5p(q^4 + 4pq^3 + 6p^2q^2 + 4p^3q + p^4)
\end{aligned}
$$

$$= 5p(q + p)^4$$ $\quad \overbrace{\text{Take out the common factor } 5p}$

$$= 5p$$ $\quad \overbrace{\text{since } q + p = 1}$

The proof in the general case follows the same pattern: the common factor is now np, and the expectation simplifies to $np(q + p)^{n-1} = np$. The details are more fiddly because of the manipulations of the binomial coefficients.

ACTIVITY

If you want a challenge write out the details of the proof that if $X \sim B(n, p)$ then the expectation of X is np.

Using the binomial distribution

AVONFORD STAR

Calvin's Tips

If you are to be successful at the tables you must develop an insight into probability. Nobody makes money playing against the odds in the long term. Try to argue your way round this problem.

Which is more likely: that you get at least one 6 when you throw a die six times, or that you get at least two 6s when you throw it twelve times?

On a single throw of a die the probability of getting a 6 is $\frac{1}{6}$ and that of not getting a 6 is $\frac{5}{6}$.

So the probability distributions for the two situations in Calvin's problem are $B(6, \frac{1}{6})$ and $B(12, \frac{1}{6})$ giving probabilities of:

$$1 - {}^6C_0(\tfrac{5}{6})^6 = 1 - 0.335 = 0.665 \text{ (at least one 6 in six throws)}$$

and

$$1 - [{}^{12}C_0(\tfrac{5}{6})^{12} + {}^{12}C_1(\tfrac{5}{6})^{11}(\tfrac{1}{6})] = 1 - (0.112 + 0.269)$$
$$= 0.619 \text{ (at least two 6s in 12 throws)}$$

So at least one 6 in six throws is somewhat more likely.

EXAMPLE 6.3

Extensive research has shown that 1 person out of every 4 is allergic to a particular grass seed. A group of 20 university students volunteer to try out a new treatment.

(i)   What is the expectation of the number of allergic people in the group?
(ii)   What is the probability that (a) exactly two (b) no more than two of the group are allergic?
(iii) How large a sample would be needed for the probability of it containing at least one allergic person to be greater than 99.9%.
(iv)   What assumptions have you made in your answer?

SOLUTION

This situation is modelled by the binomial distribution with $n = 20$, $p = 0.25$ and $q = 0.75$. The number of allergic people is denoted by X.

(i)   Expectation $= np = 20 \times 0.25 = 5$ people.
(ii) $X \sim B(20, 0.25)$
      (a) $P(X = 2) = {}^{20}C_2(0.75)^{18}(0.25)^2 = 0.067$
      (b) $P(X \leqslant 2) = P(0) + P(1) + P(2)$
            $= (0.75)^{20} + {}^{20}C_1 (0.75)^{19}(0.25) + {}^{20}C_2 (0.75)^{18}(0.25)^2$
            $= 0.003 + 0.021 + 0.067$
            $= 0.091$
(iii) Let the sample size be n (people), so that $X \sim B(n, 0.25)$.

      The probability that none of them is allergic is

      $$P(X = 0) = (0.75)^n$$

      and so the probability that at least one is allergic is

      $$P(X \geqslant 1) = 1 - P(X = 0)$$
      $$= 1 - (0.75)^n$$

So we need $\quad 1 - (0.75)^n > 0.999$

$$(0.75)^n < 0.001$$

Solving $\quad\quad (0.75)^n = 0.001$

gives $\quad\quad n \log 0.75 = \log 0.001$

$$n = \log 0.001 \div \log 0.75$$

$$= 24.01$$

So 25 people are required.

Note

Although 24.01 is very close to 24 it would be incorrect to round down.
$1 - (0.75)^{24} = 0.998\,996\,6$ which is just less than 99.9%.

(iv) The assumptions made are:
   (a) That the sample is random. This is almost certainly untrue. University students are nearly all in the 18–25 age range and so a sample of them cannot be a random sample of the whole population. They may well also be unrepresentative of the whole population in other ways. Volunteers are seldom truly random.
   (b) That the outcome for one person is independent of that for another. This is probably true unless they are a group of friends from, say, an athletics team, where those with allergies are less likely to be members.

Does the binomial distribution really work?

EXPERIMENT

In Calvin's first case you threw a die six times (or six dice once each, which amounts to the same thing).

$X \sim B(6, \frac{1}{6})$ and this gives the probabilities in the following table.

Number of 6s	Probability
0	0.335
1	0.402
2	0.201
3	0.054
4	0.008
5	0.001
6	0.000

So if you carry out the experiment of throwing six dice 1000 times and record the number of 6s each time, you should get none about 335 times, one about 402 times and so on. What does 'about' mean? How close an agreement can you expect between experimental and theoretical results?

You could carry out the experiment with dice, but it would be very tedious even if several people shared the work. Alternatively you could simulate the experiment on a spreadsheet using a random number generator.

INVESTIGATION

This is a true story. During voting at a by-election, an exit poll of 1700 voters indicated that 50% of people had voted for the Labour Party candidate. When the real votes were counted it was found that he had in fact received 57% support.

Carry out a computer simulation of the situation and use it to decide whether the difference was likely to have occurred because of the random nature of the sample, faulty sampling techniques or other possible reasons you can think of.

EXERCISE 6B

1 In a game five dice are rolled together.
   (i) What is the probability that
       (a) all five show 1 (b) exactly three show 1 (c) none of them shows 1?
   (ii) What is the most likely number of times for 6 to show?

2 There are eight colours of Smarties which normally occur in equal proportions: red, orange, yellow, green, blue, purple, pink and brown. Veronica's mother gives each of her children 16 Smarties. Veronica says that the blue ones are much nicer than the rest and is very upset when she receives less than her fair share of them.
   (i) How many blue Smarties did Veronica expect to get?
   (ii) What was the probability that she would receive fewer blue ones than she expected?
   (iii) What was the probability that she would receive more blue ones than she expected?

3 In a particular area 30% of men and 20% of women are overweight and there are four men and three women working in an office there. Find the probability that there are
   (i) 0 (ii) 1 (iii) 2 overweight men;
   (iv) 0 (v) 1 (vi) 2 overweight women;
   (vii) 2 overweight people in the office.
   What assumption have you made in answering this question?

4 On her drive to work Stella has to go through four sets of traffic lights. She estimates that for each set the probability of her finding them red is $\frac{2}{3}$ and green $\frac{1}{3}$. (She ignores the possibility of them being amber.) Stella also estimates that when a set of lights is red she is delayed by one minute.
   (i) Find the probability of
       (a) 0 (b) 1 (c) 2 (d) 3 sets of lights being against her.
   (ii) Find the expected extra journey time due to waiting at lights.

5 A drunken man steps out of a bar into a narrow alley which runs from west to east. At each step he chooses at random whether to go east or west. After 12 steps he stops for a rest.

(i) Why is it impossible for him then to be 1 step away from the bar?

(ii) What is the probability that he is then 10 steps east of the bar?

(iii) What is his most likely position?

(iv) What is the probability that he is 4 steps away from the bar, either to the east or to the west?

(v) What is the expectation of his number of steps from the bar, ignoring which side he is on, as in part (iv).

6 Pepper moths are found in two varieties, light and dark. The proportion of dark moths increases with certain types of atmospheric pollution. At the time of the question 30% of the moths in a particular town are dark.
A research student sets a moth trap and catches nine moths, four light and five dark.

(i) What is the probability of that result for a sample of nine moths?

(ii) What is the expected number of dark moths in a sample of nine?

The next night the student's trap catches ten pepper moths.

(iii) What is the probability that the number of dark moths in this sample is the same as the expected number?

7 An insurance salesman sells policies to five men, all of identical age and in good health. According to his company's records the probability that a man of this particular age will be alive in 20 years' time is $\frac{2}{3}$. Find the probability that in 20 years' time the number of men still alive will be

(i) five

(ii) at least three

(iii) exactly two

(iv) at least one.

[Cambridge]

8 Bella Cicciona, a fortune teller, claims to be able to predict the sex of unborn children. In fact, on each occasion she is consulted, the probability that she makes a correct prediction is 0.6, independent of any other prediction.

One afternoon, Bella is consulted by ten expectant mothers. Find, correct to 2 significant figures, the probabilities that

(i) her first eight predictions are correct and her last two are wrong

(ii) she makes exactly eight correct predictions

(iii) she makes at least eight correct predictions

(iv) she makes exactly eight correct predictions given that she makes at least eight.

[MEI]

9 A general knowledge quiz has ten questions. Each question has three possible 'answers' of which one only is correct. A woman attempts the quiz by pure guesswork.
   (i) Find the probabilities that she obtains
       (a) exactly two correct answers   (b) not more than two correct answers.
   (ii) What is the most likely number of correct answers and the probability that she just achieves this number?

[MEI]

10 Five unbiased dice are thrown. Calculate the probabilities that
   (i) there will be exactly four 6s
   (ii) there will be some one number appearing exactly four times
   (iii) there will be some one number appearing exactly three times and a second number appearing twice.

[MEI]

11 There are currently 4000 million premium bonds, costing £1 each, held by investors. Each month 270 000 bonds are selected at random and a prize is allocated to each.
   (i) Show that the probability of a bond being allocated a prize in any particular month is about 1 in 15 000.
   (ii) Rachel holds 3000 bonds. Show that the probability of her winning at least one prize in any particular month is about 0.18.
   (iii) Calculate the probability that Rachel goes without a prize for a whole year.
   (iv) If all the prizes were £50 how much would Rachel expect to win, on average, in a year? What does this represent as a percentage return on her investment?
   (v) In fact premium bonds give an average return of 5.2% on the money invested. Calculate the average size of a prize.

[MEI]

12 Six fair coins are tossed and those landing heads uppermost are eliminated. The remainder are tossed again and the process of elimination is repeated. Tossing and elimination continue in this way until no coins are left.

Find the probabilities of the following events.
   (i) All six coins are eliminated in the first round.
   (ii) Exactly two coins are eliminated in the first round.
   (iii) Exactly two coins are eliminated in the first round and exactly two coins are eliminated in the second round.
   (iv) Exactly two coins are eliminated in *each* of the first three rounds.
   (v) Exactly two coins are eliminated in the first round and exactly two coins are eliminated in the *third* round.

[MEI]

13 A supermarket gets eggs from a supplier in boxes of 12. The supermarket manager is concerned at the number of eggs which are broken on arrival. She has a random sample of 100 boxes checked and the numbers of broken eggs per box are as follows.

Number of eggs broken	0	1	2	3	4	5+
Number of boxes	35	39	19	6	1	0

(i) Calculate the mean and standard deviation of the number of broken eggs in a box.

(ii) Show that a reasonable estimate for p, the probability of an egg being broken on arrival, is 0.0825. Use this figure to calculate the probability that a randomly chosen box will contain no broken eggs. How does this probability relate to the observed number of boxes which contain no broken eggs?

(iii) The manager tells the suppliers that they must reduce p to the value which will ensure that, in the long run, 75% of boxes have no broken eggs. To what value must the suppliers reduce p?

[MEI]

14 A company uses machines to manufacture wine glasses. Because of imperfections in the glass it is normal for 10% of the glasses to leave the machine cracked. The company takes regular samples of size 10 from each machine. If more than 2 glasses in a sample are cracked, they stop the machine and check that it is set correctly.

(i) What is the probability that a sample of size 10 contains

(a) 0 (b) 1 (c) 2 faulty glasses, when the machine is correctly set?

(ii) What is the probability that as a result of taking a sample a machine is stopped when it is correctly set?

(iii) A machine is in fact incorrectly set and 20% of the glasses from it are cracked. What is the probability that this is undetected by a particular sample?

The binomial distribution may be used to model situations in which:

1 you are conducting trials on random samples of a certain size, n
2 there are two possible outcomes, often referred to as success and failure
3 both outcomes have fixed probabilities, p and q, and $p + q = 1$
4 the probability of success in any trial is independent of the outcomes of previous trials
5 The probability that the number of successes, X, has the value r, is given by

$$P(X = r) = {}^nC_r q^{n-r} p^r.$$

6 For $B(n, p)$ the expectation of the number of successes is np.

To be and not to be, that is the answer.

Piet Hein

7

Hypothesis testing using the binomial distribution

You may prove anything by figures.

An anonymous salesman

THE AVONFORD STAR

Machoman Dan

Beer drinking Dan Ellis has just become a father for the eighth time, and they are ALL BOYS.

Find Dan at his local and he will tell you that having no girls among the eight shows that he is a real man.

'When I was just a lad at school I said I had macho chromosomes,' Dan claims.

'Now I have been proved right.'

Cheers! Dan Ellis reckons his all-boy offspring prove he's a real man

What do you think?

There are two quite different points here.

The first is that you have probably decided that Dan is a male chauvinist, preferring boys to girls. However, you should not let your views on that influence your judgement on the second point, his claim to be biologically different from other people, with special chromosomes.

There are two ways this claim could be investigated, to look at his chromosomes under a high magnification microscope or to consider the statistical evidence. Since you have neither Dan Ellis nor a suitable microscope to hand, you must resort to the latter.

If you have eight children you would expect them to be divided about evenly between the sexes, 4 − 4, 5 − 3 or perhaps 6 − 2. When you realised that a baby was on its way you would think it equally likely to be a boy or a girl until it were born, or a scan were carried out, when you would know for certain one way or the other.

In other words you would say that the probability of its being a boy was 0.5 and that of its being a girl 0.5. So you can model the number of boys among eight children by the binomial distribution B(8, 0.5).

This gives these probabilities, shown in figure 7.1.

Boys	Girls	Probability
0	8	$\frac{1}{256}$
1	7	$\frac{8}{256}$
2	6	$\frac{28}{256}$
3	5	$\frac{56}{256}$
4	4	$\frac{70}{256}$
5	3	$\frac{56}{256}$
6	2	$\frac{28}{256}$
7	1	$\frac{8}{256}$
8	0	$\frac{1}{256}$

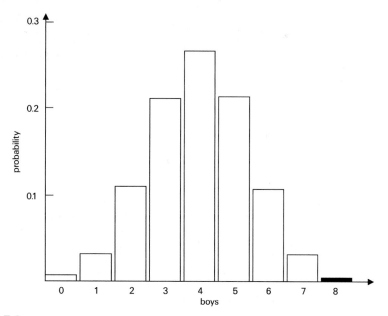

Figure 7.1

So you can say that, if a biologically normal man fathers eight children, the probability that they will all be boys is $\frac{1}{256}$ (shaded in figure 7.1).

This is unlikely but by no means impossible.

Note

The probability of a baby being a boy is not in fact 0.5 but about 0.503. Boys are less tough than girls and so more likely to die in infancy and this seems to be nature's way of compensating. In most societies men have a markedly lower life expectancy as well.

❓ You may think Dan Ellis a thoroughly objectionable character but in some countries large sections of society value boy children more highly than girls. Medical advances mean that it will soon be possible to decide in advance the sex of your next baby. What would be the effect of this on a country's population if, say, half the parents decided to have only boys and the other half to let nature take its course?

(This is a real problem. The social consequences could be devastating.)

Defining terms

In the last example we investigated Dan Ellis's claim by comparing it to the usual situation, the unexceptional. If we use p for the probability that a child is a boy then the normal state of affairs can be stated as

$$p = 0.5.$$

This is called the *null hypothesis*, denoted by H_0.

Dan's claim (made, he says, before he had any children) was that

$$p > 0.5$$

and this is called the *alternative hypothesis*, H_1.

The word hypothesis (plural *hypotheses*) means a theory which is put forward either for the sake of argument or because it is believed or suspected to be true. An investigation like this is usually conducted in the form of a test, called a *hypothesis test*. There are many different sorts of hypothesis test used in statistics; in this chapter you meet only one of them.

It is never possible to prove something statistically in the sense that, for example, you can prove that the angle sum of a triangle is $180°$. Even if you tossed a coin a million times and it came down heads every single time, it is still possible that the coin is unbiased and just happened to land that way. What you can say is that it is very unlikely; the probability of it happening that way is $(0.5)^{1\,000\,000}$ which is a decimal that starts with over $300\,000$ zeros. This is so tiny that you would feel quite confident in declaring the coin biased.

There comes a point when the probability is so small that you say 'That's good enough for me. I am satisfied that it hasn't happened that way by chance.'

The probability at which you make that decision is called the *significance level* of the test. Significance levels are usually given as percentages; 0.05 is written as 5%, 0.01 as 1% and so on.

So in the case of Dan Ellis, the question could have been worded:

Test, at the 1% significance level, Dan Ellis's boyhood claim that his children are more likely to be boys than girls.

The answer would then look like this:

Null hypothesis, H_0: $p = 0.5$ (boys and girls are equally likely)
Alternative hypothesis, H_1: $p > 0.5$ (boys are more likely)
Significance level: 1%

Probability of 8 boys from 8 children $= \frac{1}{256} = 0.0039 = 0.39\%$.

Since $0.39\% < 1\%$ we reject the null hypothesis and accept the alternative hypothesis. We accept Dan Ellis's claim.

This example also illustrates some of the problems associated with hypothesis testing. Here is a list of points you should be considering.

Hypothesis testing checklist

1 Was the test set up before or after the data were known?

The test consists of a null hypothesis, an alternative hypothesis and a significance level.

In this case, the null hypothesis is the natural state of affairs and so does not really need to be stated in advance. Dan's claim 'When I was just a lad at school I said I had macho chromosomes' could be interpreted as the alternative hypothesis, $p > 0.5$.

The problem is that one suspects that whatever children Dan had he would find an excuse to boast. If they had all been girls, he might have been talking about 'my irresistible attraction for the opposite sex' and if they had been a mixture of girls and boys he would have been claiming 'super-virility' just because he had eight children.

Any test carried out retrospectively must be treated with suspicion.

2 Was the sample involved chosen at random and are the data independent?

The sample was not random and that may have been inevitable. If Dan had lots of children around the country with different mothers, a random sample of eight could have been selected. However, we have no knowledge that this is the case.

The data are the sexes of Dans' children. If there are no multiple births (for example, identical twins), then they are independent.

3 Is the statistical procedure actually testing the original claim?

Dan Ellis claims to have 'macho chromosomes' whereas the statistical test is of the alternative hypothesis that $p > 0.5$. The two are not necessarily the same. Even if this alternative hypothesis is true, it does not necessarily follow that Dan has macho chromosomes.

The ideal hypothesis test

In the ideal hypothesis test you take the following steps, in this order:

1 Establish the null and alternative hypotheses.
2 Decide on the significance level.
3 Collect suitable data using a random sampling procedure that ensures the items are independent.
4 Conduct the test, doing the necessary calculations.
5 Interpret the result in terms of the original claim, theory or problem.

There are times, however, when you need to carry out a test but it is just not possible to do so as rigorously as this.

In the case of Dan Ellis, you would require him to go away and father eight more children, this time with randomly selected mothers, which is clearly impossible. Had Dan been a laboratory rat and not a human, however, you probably could have organised it.

Choosing the significance level

If, instead of 1%, we had set the significance level at 0.1%, then we would have rejected Dan's claim, since 0.39% > 0.1%. The lower the percentage in the significance level, the more stringent is the test.

The significance level you choose for a test involves a balanced judgement.

Imagine that you are testing the rivets on an plane's wing to see if they have lost their strength. Setting a small significance level, say 0.1%, means that you will only declare the rivets weak if you are very confident of your finding. The trouble with requiring such a high level of evidence is that even when they are weak you may well fail to register the fact, with the possible consequence that the plane crashes. On the other hand if you set a high significance level, such as 10%, you run the risk of declaring the rivets faulty when they are all right, involving the company in expensive and unnecessary maintenance work.

The question of how you choose the best significance level is, however, beyond the scope of this introductory chapter.

EXAMPLE 7.1

Here is another example, from 'Calvin's Tips' in the *Avonford Star*. Cover up the solution and then, as you work your way through it, see if you can predict the next step at each stage.

Does the procedure follow the steps of the ideal hypothesis test?

THE AVONFORD STAR

Calvin's Tips

I was at a casino the other evening. After several hours' play, a lady whom I shall call Leonora had lost a lot of money. She complained to the management that one of the dice was biased, with a tendency to show the number 1.

The management agreed to test the die at the 5% significance level, throwing it 20 times. If the test supported Leonora's view she would get her money refunded, otherwise she would be asked to leave the premises and never return.

The results were as follows

1	6	6	5	5
1	2	3	2	3
4	4	4	1	4
1	1	4	1	3

What happened to my friend Leonora?

SOLUTION

Let p be the probability of getting 1 on any throw of the die.

Null hypothesis, H_0: $p = \frac{1}{6}$ (The die is unbiased)

Alternative hypothesis, H_1: $p > \frac{1}{6}$ (The die is biased towards 1)

Significance level: 5%

The results may be summarised as follows:

Score	1	2	3	4	5	6
Frequency	6	2	3	5	2	2

Under the null hypothesis, the number of 1s obtained is modelled by the binomial distribution, B$(20, \frac{1}{6})$ which gives these probabilities:

Number of 1s	Expression	Probability
0	$(\frac{5}{6})^{20}$	0.0261
1	$^{20}C_1 (\frac{5}{6})^{19}(\frac{1}{6})$	0.1043
2	$^{20}C_2 (\frac{5}{6})^{18}(\frac{1}{6})^2$	0.1982
3	$^{20}C_3 (\frac{5}{6})^{17}(\frac{1}{6})^3$	0.2379
4	$^{20}C_4 (\frac{5}{6})^{16}(\frac{1}{6})^4$	0.2022
5	$^{20}C_5 (\frac{5}{6})^{15}(\frac{1}{6})^5$	0.1294
6	$^{20}C_6 (\frac{5}{6})^{14}(\frac{1}{6})^6$	0.0647
7	$^{20}C_7 (\frac{5}{6})^{13}(\frac{1}{6})^7$	0.0259
8	$^{20}C_8 (\frac{5}{6})^{12}(\frac{1}{6})^8$	0.0084
$\vdots$	$\vdots$	$\vdots$
20	$(\frac{1}{6})^{20}$	0.0000

The probability of 1 coming up between 0 and 5 times is found by adding these probabilities to get 0.8981

If you worked out all these and added them you would get the probability that the number of 1s is 6 or more (up to a possible 20). It is much quicker, however, to find this as $1 - 0.8981$ (the answer above) $= 0.1019$

Calling X the number of 1s occurring when a die is rolled 20 times, the probability of six or more 1s is given by

$$P(X \geqslant 6) = 1 - P(X \leqslant 5) = 1 - 0.8981 = 0.1019,$$

about 10%.

Since $10\% > 5\%$, the null hypothesis (the die is unbiased) is accepted.

The probability of a result at least as extreme as that observed is greater than the 5% cut off that was set in advance, that is, greater than the chosen significance level.

The alternative hypothesis (the die is biased in favour of the number 1) is rejected, even though the number 1 did come up more often than the other numbers.

THE AVONFORD STAR

Leonora did not get her money back but the management relented and did not ban her from the Casino.

Note

Notice that this is a test not of the particular result (six 1s) but of a result at least as extreme as this (at least six 1s), the area shaded in figure 7.2. A hypothesis test deals with the probability of an event 'as unusual as or more unusual than' what has occurred.

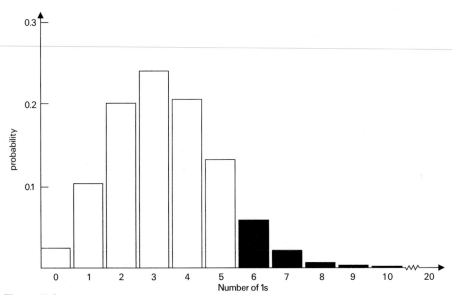

Figure 7.2

Another method

You could have found the probability of up to five scores of 1 using *Cumulative Binomial Probability* tables. These give $P(X \leqslant x)$ when $X \sim B(n, p)$ for $x = 0, 1, 2, \ldots, n$ and values of p from 0.05 to 0.95 at intervals of 0.05 plus $\frac{1}{6}, \frac{1}{3}, \frac{2}{3}, \frac{5}{6}$. There is a separate table for each value of n from 1 to 20. Look up under $n = 20$.

n	p / x	0.050	0.100	0.150	$\frac{1}{6}$	0.200	0.250	0.300	$\frac{1}{3}$	0.350
20	0	0.3585	0.1216	0.0388	0.0261	0.0115	0.0032	0.0008	0.0003	0.0002
	1	0.7358	0.3917	0.1756	0.1304	0.0692	0.0243	0.0076	0.0033	0.0021
	2	0.9245	0.6769	0.4049	0.3287	0.2061	0.0913	0.0355	0.0176	0.0121
	3	0.9841	0.8670	0.6477	0.5665	0.4114	0.2252	0.1071	0.0604	0.0444
	4	0.9974	0.9568	0.8298	0.7687	0.6296	0.4148	0.2375	0.1515	0.1182
	5	0.9997	0.9887	0.9327	0.8982	0.8042	0.6172	0.4164	0.2972	0.2454
	6	1.0000	0.9976	0.9781	0.9629	0.9133	0.7858	0.6080	0.4973	0.4166
	7		0.9996	0.9941	0.9887	0.9679	0.8982	0.7723	0.6615	0.6010
	8		0.9999	0.9987	0.9972	0.9900	0.9591	0.8867	0.8095	0.7624
	9		1.0000	0.9998	0.9994	0.9974	0.9861	0.9520	0.9081	0.8782
	10			1.0000	0.9999	0.9994	0.9961	0.9829	0.9624	0.9468
	11				1.0000	0.9999	0.9991	0.9949	0.9870	0.9804
	12					1.0000	0.9998	0.9987	0.9963	0.9940
	13						1.0000	0.9997	0.9991	0.9985
	14							1.0000	0.9998	0.9997
	15								1.0000	1.0000

In this case $p = \frac{1}{6}$ so the probability of up to five scores of 1 is 0.8982, the same result as before apart from the last figure where there is a difference of 1 from rounding.

 Look in the table. Just below 0.8982 is 0.9629. What information is given by $0.9629 - 0.8982 = 0.0647$?

In all these questions you should apply this checklist to the hypothesis test:

1 Was the test set up before or after the data were known?
2 Was the sample used for the test chosen at random and are the data independent?
3 Is the statistical procedure actually testing the original claim?

You should also comment critically on whether these steps have been followed:

1 Establish the null and alternative hypotheses.
2 Decide on the significance level.

3 Collect suitable data using a random sampling procedure that ensures the items are independent.

4 Conduct the test, doing the necessary calculations.

5 Interpret the result in terms of the original claim, theory or problem.

1 Mrs da Silva is running for President. She claims to have 60% of the population supporting her.

She is suspected of overestimating her support and a random sample of 20 people are asked whom they support. Only nine say Mrs da Silva.

Test, at the 5% significance level, the hypothesis that she has overestimated her support.

2 A driving instructor claims that 60% of his pupils pass their driving test at the first attempt. Supposing this claim is true, find, using tables or otherwise, the probability that, of 20 pupils taking their first test

(i) exactly 12 pass

(ii) more than 12 pass.

A local newspaper reporter suspects that the driving instructor is exaggerating his success rate and so she decides to carry out a statistical investigation. State the null and alternative hypotheses which she is testing. She contacts 20 of his pupils who have recently taken their first test and discovers that N passed. Given that she performs a 5% significance test and that she concludes that the driving instructor's claim was exaggerated, what are the possible values of N?

[MEI]

3 A company developed synthetic coffee and claim that coffee drinkers could not distinguish it from the real product. A number of coffee drinkers challenged the company's claim, saying that the synthetic coffee tasted synthetic. In a test, carried out by an independent consumer protection body, 20 people were given a mug of coffee. Ten had the synthetic brand and ten the natural, but they were not told which they had been given.

Out of the ten given the synthetic brand, eight said it was synthetic and two said it was natural. Use this information to test the coffee drinkers' claim (as against the null hypothesis of the company's claim), at the 5% significance level.

4 A group of 18 students decides to investigate the truth of the saying that if you drop a piece of toast it is more likely to land butter-side down. They each take one piece of toast, butter it on one side and throw it in the air. Eleven land butter-side down, the rest butter-side up. Use their results to carry out a hypothesis test at the 10% significance level, stating clearly your null and alternative hypotheses.

5 On average 70% of people pass their driving test first time. There are complaints that Mr McTaggart is too harsh and so, unknown to himself, his work is monitored. It is found that he fails 10 out of 20 candidates. Are the complaints justified at the 5% significance level?

6   A machine makes bottles. In normal running 5% of the bottles are expected to be cracked, but if the machine needs servicing this proportion will increase. As part of a routine check, 50 bottles are inspected and 5 are found to be unsatisfactory. Does this provide evidence, at the 5% significance level, that the machine needs servicing?

7   A firm producing mugs has a quality control scheme in which a random sample of 10 mugs from each batch is inspected. For 50 such samples, the numbers of defective mugs are as follows:

Number of defective mugs	0	1	2	3	4	5	6+
Number of samples	5	13	15	12	4	1	0

   (i)   Find the mean and standard deviation of the number of defective mugs per sample.

   (ii) Show that a reasonable estimate for p, the probability that a mug is defective, is 0.2. Use this figure to calculate the probability that a randomly chosen sample will contain exactly two defective mugs. Comment on the agreement between this value and the observed data.

The management is not satisfied with 20% of mugs being defective and introduces a new process to reduce the proportion of defective mugs.

   (iii) A random sample of 20 mugs, produced by the new process, contains just one which is defective. Test, at the 5% level, whether it is reasonable to suppose that the proportion of defective mugs has been reduced, stating your null and alternative hypotheses clearly.

   (iv) What would the conclusion have been if the management had chosen to conduct the test at the 10% level?

[MEI]

8   An annual mathematics contest contains 15 questions, 5 short and 10 long.
   The probability that I get a short question right is 0.9.
   The probability that I get a long question right is 0.5.
   My performances on questions are independent of each other.
   Find the probability of the following:

   (i)   I get all the 5 short questions right

   (ii) I get exactly 8 of the 10 long questions right

   (iii) I get exactly 3 of the short questions and all of the long questions right

   (iv) I get exactly 13 of the 15 questions right.

After some practice, I hope that my performance on the long questions will improve this year. I intend to carry out an appropriate hypothesis test.

   (v)   State suitable null and alternative hypotheses for the test.

In this year's contest I get exactly 8 of the 10 long questions right.

   (vi) Is there sufficient evidence, at the 5% significance level, that my performance on long questions has improved?

Critical values and critical regions

In Example 7.1 the number 1 came up six times and this was not enough to get poor Leonora a refund. What was the least number of times 1 would have had to come up for the test to give the opposite result?

We again use X to denote the number of times 1 comes up in the 20 throws and so $X = 6$ means that the number 1 comes up six times.

We know from our earlier work that the probability that $X \leqslant 5$ is 0.8982 and we can use the binomial distribution to work out the probabilities that $X = 6$, $X = 7$, etc.

$$P(X = 6) = {}^{20}C_6(\tfrac{5}{6})^{14}(\tfrac{1}{6})^6 = 0.0647$$
$$P(X = 7) = {}^{20}C_7(\tfrac{5}{6})^{13}(\tfrac{1}{6})^7 = 0.0259$$

We know $P(X \geqslant 6) = 1 - P(X \leqslant 5) = 1 - 0.8982 = 0.1018$.

0.1018 is a little over 10% and so greater than the significance level of 5%. There is no reason to reject H_0.

What about the case when the number 1 comes up seven times, that is $X = 7$?

$$\text{Since } P(X \leqslant 6) = P(X \leqslant 5) + P(X = 6)$$
$$P(X \leqslant 6) = 0.8982 + 0.0647 = 0.9629$$

$$\text{So } P(X \geqslant 7) = 1 - P(X \leqslant 6)$$
$$= 1 - 0.9629 = 0.0371 = 3.71\%$$

Since 3.7% < 5% H_0 is now rejected in favour of H_1.

You can see that Leonora needed the 1 to come up seven or more times if her case was to be upheld. She missed by just one. You might think Leonora's 'all or nothing' test was a bit harsh. Sometimes tests are designed so that if the result falls within a certain region further trials are recommended.

In this example the number 7 is the *critical value* (at the 5% significance level), the value at which you change from accepting the null hypothesis to rejecting it. The range of values for which you reject the null hypothesis, in this case $X \geqslant 7$, is called the *critical region*.

It is sometimes easier in hypothesis testing to find the critical region and see if your value lies in it, rather than working out the probability of a value at least as extreme as the one you have, the procedure used so far.

The quality control department of a factory tests a random sample of 20 items from each batch produced. A batch is rejected (or perhaps subject to further tests) if the number of faulty items in the sample, X, is more than 2.

This means that the critical region is $X \geqslant 3$.

It is much simpler for the operator carrying out the test to be told the critical region (determined in advance by the person designing the procedure) than to have to work out a probability for each test result.

> **Test procedure**
>
> **Take 20 pistons**
>
> If 3 or more are faulty REJECT the batch

EXAMPLE 7.2

World-wide 25% of men are colour-blind but it is believed that the condition is less widespread among a group of remote hill tribes. An anthropologist plans to test this by sending field workers to visit villages in that area. In each village 30 men are to be tested for colour-blindness. Find the critical region for the test at the 5% level of significance.

SOLUTION

Let p be the probability that a man in that area is colour-blind.

Null hypothesis, H_0: $\qquad p = 0.25$
Alternative hypothesis, H_1: $\quad p < 0.25$ (Less colour-blindness in this area)
Significance level: $\qquad\qquad$ 5%

With the hypothesis H_0, if the number of colour-blind men in a sample of 30 is X, then $X \sim B(30, 0.25)$.

The critical region is the region $X \leqslant k$, where

$$P(X \leqslant k) \leqslant 0.05 \quad \text{and} \quad P(X \leqslant k+1) > 0.05.$$

Since $n = 30$ is too large for the available tables we have to calculate the probabilities:

$$P(X = 0) = (0.75)^{30} = 0.00018$$
$$P(X = 1) = 30\,(0.75)^{29}(0.25) = 0.00179$$
$$P(X = 2) = {}^{30}C_2\,(0.75)^{28}(0.25)^2 = 0.00863$$
$$P(X = 3) = {}^{30}C_3\,(0.75)^{27}(0.25)^3 = 0.02685$$
$$P(X = 4) = {}^{30}C_4\,(0.75)^{26}(0.25)^4 = 0.06042.$$

So $\qquad P(X \leqslant 3) = 0.00018 + 0.00179 + 0.00863 + 0.02685 \approx 0.0375 \leqslant 0.05$

but $\qquad P(X \leqslant 4) \approx 0.0929 > 0.05.$

Therefore the critical region is $X \leqslant 3$.

What is the critical region at the 10% significance level?

In many other hypothesis tests it is usual to find the critical values from tables. Later books in this series cover several such tests.

EXPERIMENTS

MIND READING

Here is a simple experiment to see if you can read the mind of a friend whom you know well. The two of you face each other across a table on which is placed a coin. Your friend takes the coin and puts it in one or other hand under the table. You have to guess which one.

Play this game at least 20 times and test at the 10% significance level whether you can read your friend's mind.

SMARTIES

Get a large box of Smarties and taste the different colours. Choose the colour, C, which you think has the most distinctive flavour.

Now close your eyes and get a friend to feed you Smarties. Taste each one and say if it is your chosen colour or not. Do this for at least 20 Smarties and test at the 10% significance level whether you can pick out those with colour C by taste.

LEFT AND RIGHT

It is said that if people are following a route which brings them to a T-junction where they have a free choice between turning left and right the majority will turn right.

Design and carry out an experiment to test this hypothesis.

Note

This is taken very seriously by companies choosing stands at exhibitions. It is considered worth paying extra for a location immediately to the right of one of the entrances.

EXERCISE 7B

1 A leaflet from the Department of Health recently claimed that 70% of businesses operate a no smoking policy on their premises. A member of the public who believed the true figure to be lower than 70% rang a random sample of 19 businesses to ask whether or not they operated a no smoking policy. She then carried out a hypothesis test.

(i) Write down the null and alternative hypotheses under test.

(ii) Of the 19 businesses, k say that they do operate a no smoking policy. Use tables to write down the critical region for a 10% test. (That is, write down the values of k for which the null hypothesis would be rejected at the 10% level of significance.)

(iii) A second person decided to carry out a similar test, also at the 10% level, but sampled only four businesses. Write down the critical region in this case.

(iv) Find, for each test, the probability that the null hypothesis is rejected if the true figure is 65%. Hence state which of the two tests is preferable and explain why.

[MEI]

2 In a certain country, 90% of letters are delivered the day after posting.

A resident posts eight letters on a certain day.

Find the probability that
(i)   all eight letters are delivered the next day
(ii) at least six letters are delivered the next day
(iii) exactly half the letters are delivered the next day.

It is later suspected that the service has deteriorated as a result of mechanisation. To test this, 17 letters are posted and it is found that only 13 of them arrive the next day. Let p denote the probability, after mechanisation, that a letter is delivered the next day.
(iv) Write down suitable null and alternative hypotheses for the value of p.
(v)   Carry out the hypothesis test, at the 5% level of significance, stating your results clearly.
(vi) Write down the critical region for the test, giving a reason for your choice.

[MEI]

3 For most small birds, the ratio of males to females may be expected to be about 1:1. In one ornithological study birds are trapped by setting fine-mesh nets. The trapped birds are counted and then released. The catch may be regarded as a random sample of the birds in the area.

The ornithologists want to test whether there are more male blackbirds than females.
(i)   Assuming that the sex ratio of blackbirds is 1:1, find the probability that a random sample of 16 blackbirds contains
     (a) 12 males   (b) at least 12 males.
(ii) State the null and alternative hypotheses the ornithologists should use.

In one sample of 16 blackbirds there are 12 males and 4 females.
(iii) Carry out a suitable test using these data at the 5% significance level, stating your conclusion clearly. Find the critical region for the test.

(iv) Another ornithologist points out that, because female birds spend much time sitting on the nest, females are less likely to be caught than males. Explain how this would affect your conclusions.

[MEI]

4 A seed supplier advertises that, on average, 80% of a certain type of seed will germinate. Suppose that 18 of these seeds, chosen at random, are planted.

(i) Find the probability that 17 or more seeds will germinate if
   (a) the supplier's claim is correct
   (b) the supplier is incorrect and 82% of the seeds, on average, germinate.

Mr Brewer is the advertising manager for the seed supplier. He thinks that the germination rate may be higher than 80% and he decides to carry out a hypothesis test at the 10% level of significance. He plants 18 seeds.

(ii) Write down the null and alternative hypotheses for Mr Brewer's test, explaining why the alternative hypothesis takes the form it does.

(iii) Find the critical region for Mr Brewer's test. Explain your reasoning.

(iv) Determine the probability that Mr Brewer will reach the *wrong* conclusion if
   (a) the true germination rate is 80%
   (b) the true germination rate is 82%.

[MEI]

1-tail and 2-tail tests

Think back to the two examples in the first part of this chapter.

What would Dan have said if his eight children had all been girls?
What would Leonora have said if the number 1 had not come up at all?

In both our examples the claim was not only that something was unusual but that it was so in a particular direction. So we looked only at one side of the distributions when working out the probabilities, as you can see in figure 7.1 on page 157 and figure 7.2 on page 162. In both cases we applied 1-tail tests. (The word tail refers to the shaded part at the end of the distribution.)

If Dan had just claimed that there was something odd about his chromosomes, then you would have had to work out the probability of a result as extreme on either side of the distribution, in this case eight girls or eight boys, and you would then apply a 2-tail test.

Here is an example of a 2-tail test.

EXAMPLE 7.3

The producer of a television programme claims that it is politically unbiased. 'If you take somebody off the street it is 50:50 whether he or she will say the programme favours the government or the opposition', she says.

However, when ten people, selected at random, are asked the question 'Does the programme support the government or the opposition?', nine say it supports the government.

Does this constitute evidence, at the 5% significance level, that the producer's claim is inaccurate?

SOLUTION

Read the last sentence carefully and you will see that it does not say in which direction the bias must be. It does not ask if the programme is favouring the government or the opposition, only if the producer's claim is inaccurate. So you must consider both ends of the distribution, working out the probability of such an extreme result either way; 9 or 10 saying it favours the government, or 9 or 10 the opposition. This is a 2-tail test.

If p is the probability that somebody believes the programme supports the government, you have

Null hypothesis, H_0: $\quad\quad p = 0.5 \quad$ (Claim accurate)
Alternative hypothesis, H_1: $\quad p \neq 0.5 \quad$ (Claim inaccurate)
Significance level: $\quad\quad\quad 5\%$
$\quad\quad\quad\quad\quad\quad\quad\quad\quad$ 2-tail test

The situation is modelled by the binomial distribution B(10, 0.5) and is shown in figure 7.3.

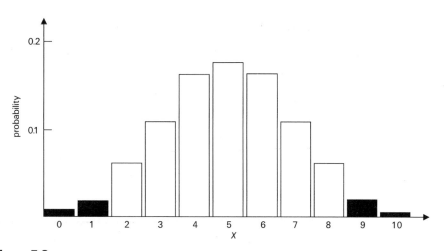

Figure 7.3

This gives

$$P(X = 0) = \frac{1}{1024} \quad\quad P(X = 1) = \frac{10}{1024}$$

$$P(X = 10) = \frac{1}{1024} \quad\quad P(X = 9) = \frac{10}{1024}$$

where X is the number of people saying the programme favours the government. Thus the total probability for the two tails is $\frac{22}{1024}$ or 2.15%.

Since 2.15% < 5% the null hypothesis is rejected in favour of the alternative, *that the producer's claim is inaccurate.*

Note

You have to look carefully at the way a test is worded to decide if it should be 1-tail or 2-tail.

Dan Ellis claimed his chromosomes made him *more* likely to father boys than girls. That requires a 1-tail test.

In Calvin's story, Leonora claimed the die was biased in the direction of *too many* 1s. Again a 1-tail test.

The test of the television producer's claim was for *inaccuracy* in *either* direction and so a 2-tail test was needed.

Asymmetrical cases

In the example above the distribution was symmetrical and so the 2-tail test was quite simple to apply. In the next case the distribution is not symmetrical and the test has to be carried out by finding out the critical regions at each tail.

EXAMPLE 7.4

Pepper moths occur in two varieties, light and dark. The proportion of dark moths increases with certain types of atmospheric pollution.

In a particular village, 25% of the moths are dark, the rest light. A biologist wants to use them as a pollution indicator. She traps samples of 15 moths and counts how many of them are dark.

For what numbers of dark moths among the 15 can she say, at the 10% significance level, that the pollution level is changing?

SOLUTION

In this question you are asked to find the critical region for the test:

H_0: $p = 0.25$ (the proportion of dark moths is 25%)
H_1: $p \neq 0.25$ (the proportion is no longer 25%)
        Significance level 10%
        2-tail test

where p is the probability that a moth selected at random is dark.

You want to find each tail to be as nearly as possible 5% but both must be less than 5%, something that is easiest done using cumulative binomial distribution tables.

Look under $n = 15$, for $p = 0.25$.

n	$\overset{p}{\underset{x}{\diagdown}}$	0.050	0.100	0.150	1/6	0.200	0.250	0.300	1/3	0.350	0.400
15	0	0.4633	0.2059	0.0874	0.0649	0.0352	0.0134	0.0047	0.0023	0.0016	0.0005
	1	0.8290	0.5490	0.3186	0.2596	0.1671	0.0802	0.0353	0.0194	0.0142	0.0052
	2	0.9638	0.8159	0.6042	0.5322	0.3980	0.2361	0.1268	0.0794	0.0617	0.0271
	3	0.9945	0.9444	0.8227	0.7685	0.6482	0.4613	0.2969	0.2092	0.1727	0.0905
	4	0.9994	0.9873	0.9383	0.9102	0.8358	0.6865	0.5155	0.4041	0.3519	0.2173
	5	0.9999	0.9978	0.9832	0.9726	0.9389	0.8516	0.7216	0.6184	0.5643	0.4032
	6	1.0000	0.9997	0.9964	0.9934	0.9819	0.9434	0.8689	0.7970	0.7548	0.6098
	7		1.0000	0.9994	0.9987	0.9958	0.9827	0.9500	0.9118	0.8868	0.7869
	8			0.9999	0.9998	0.9992	0.9958	0.9848	0.9692	0.9578	0.9050
	9			1.0000	1.0000	0.9999	0.9992	0.9963	0.9915	0.9876	0.9662
	10					1.0000	0.9999	0.9993	0.9982	0.9972	0.9907
	11						1.0000	0.9999	0.9997	0.9995	0.9981
	12							1.0000	1.0000	0.9999	0.9997
	13									1.0000	1.0000
	14										
	15										

From this you can see that the left-hand tail includes 0 but not 1 or more; the right-hand tail is 8 and above but not 7.

So the critical regions are less than 1 and more than 7 dark moths in the 20. For these values she would claim the pollution level is changing.

Note

This is really quite a crude test. The left-hand tail is 1.34%, the right-hand $(1 - 0.9827)$ or 1.73%. Neither is close to 5%. This situation would be improved if you were to increase the sample size; 15 is a small number of moths on which to base your findings. However, for large samples you would expect to use either the normal or the Poisson approximation to the binomial distribution; you will meet these in *Statistics 2*.

EXERCISE 7C

1 To test the claim that a coin is biased, it is tossed 20 times. It comes down heads 12 times. Test at the 10% significance level whether this claim is justified.

2 A biologist discovers a colony of a previously unknown type of bird nesting in a cave. Out of the 16 chicks which hatch during his period of investigation, 13 are female. Test at the 5% significance level whether this supports the view that the sex ratio for the chicks differs from 1.

3 People entering an exhibition have to choose whether to turn left or right. Out of the first twelve people, nine turn left and three right. Test at the 5% significance level whether people are more likely to turn one way than another.

4 Weather records for a certain seaside resort show that on average one day in four in April is wet, but local people write to their newspaper complaining that the climate is changing.

A reporter on the paper records the weather for the next 20 days in April and finds that 10 of them are wet.

Do you think the complaint is justified?

5 In a fruit machine there are five drums which rotate independently to show one out of six types of fruit each (lemon, apple, orange, melon, banana and pear). You win a prize if all five stop showing the same fruit. A customer claims that the machine is fixed; the lemon in the first place is not showing the right number of times. The manager runs the machine 20 times and the lemon shows 6 times in the first place. Is the customer's complaint justified at the 10% significance level?

6 A boy is losing in a game of cards and claims that his opponent is cheating.

Out of the last 12 times he shuffled and dealt the cards, the first card to be laid down was a spade on only one occasion. Can he justify his claim at the 2% significance level?

7 A small colony of 20 individuals of a previously unknown animal is discovered. It is believed it might be the same species as one described by early explorers who said that one-quarter of them were male, the rest female.

What numbers of males and females would lead you to believe, at the 5% significance level, that they are not the same species?

8 A multiple choice test has 20 questions, with the answer for each allowing four options, *A*, *B*, *C* and *D*. All the students in a class tell their teacher that they guessed all 20 answers. The teacher does not believe them. Devise a 2-tail test at the 10% significance level to apply to a student's mark to test the hypothesis that the answers were not selected at random.

9 When a certain language is written down, 15% of the letters are Z. Use this information to devise a test at the 10% significance level which somebody who does not know the language could apply to a short passage, 50 letters long, to determine whether it is written in the same language.

10 A seed firm states on the packets of bean seeds that the germination rate is 80%. Each packet contains 25 seeds.
   (i) How many seeds would you expect to germinate out of one packet?
   (ii) What is the probability of exactly 17 germinating?

A man buys a packet and only 12 germinate.
   (iii) Is he justified in complaining?

11 Given that X has a binomial distribution in which $n = 15$ and $p = 0.5$, find the probability of each of the following events.

(i) $X = 4$

(ii) $X \leqslant 4$

(iii) $X = 4$ or $X = 11$

(iv) $X \leqslant 4$ or $X \geqslant 11$

A large company is considering introducing a new selection procedure for job applicants. The selection procedure is intended to result over a long period in equal numbers of men and women being offered jobs. The new procedure is tried with a random sample of applicants and 15 of them, 11 women and 4 men, are offered jobs.

(v) Carry out a suitable test at the 5% level of significance to determine whether it is reasonable to suppose that the selection procedure is performing as intended. You should state the null and alternative hypotheses under test and explain carefully how you arrive at your conclusions.

(vi) Suppose now that, of the 15 applicants offered jobs, w are women. Find all the values of w for which the selection procedure should be judged acceptable at the 5% level.

[MEI]

KEY POINTS

1 Hypothesis testing checklist
- Was the test set up before or after the data were known?
- Was the sample involved chosen at random and are the data independent?
- Is the statistical procedure actually testing the original claim?

2 Steps for conducting a hypothesis test
- Establish the null and alternative hypotheses.
- Decide on the significance level.
- Collect suitable data using a random sampling procedure that ensures the items are independent.
- Conduct the test, doing the necessary calculations.
- Interpret the result in terms of the original claim, theory or problem.

Appendices

1 The derivation of the alternative form of the variance

$$\text{Variance} = \frac{1}{n} \sum (x - \bar{x})^2$$

$$= \frac{1}{n} \sum (x^2 - 2x\bar{x} + \bar{x}^2)$$

$$= \frac{1}{n} \sum x^2 - \frac{1}{n} \sum 2x\bar{x} + \frac{1}{n} \sum \bar{x}^2$$

$$= \frac{1}{n} \sum x^2 - 2\bar{x} \frac{1}{n} \sum x + \frac{1}{n} n\bar{x}^2$$

$$= \frac{1}{n} \sum x^2 - 2\bar{x}^2 + \bar{x}^2$$

$$= \frac{1}{n} \sum x^2 - \bar{x}^2$$

2 The binomial theorem

A typical binomial expression may be written $(x + y)^n$.

'Binomial' means 'two numbers' and these are x and y. When the binomial expression is used to find a probability distribution, n is a positive whole number and x and y represent probabilities adding up to 1.

There are two common ways of expanding, or multiplying out, a binomial expression: by using Pascal's triangle or the formula for ^nC_r.

Pascal's triangle

If you multiply out $(x + y)^4$, you get $1x^4 + 4x^3y + 6x^2y^2 + 4xy^3 + 1y^4$. You can find the various coefficients in this expression $(1, 4, 6, 4, 1)$ by looking along row 4 of Pascal's triangle:

Row												
0						1						
1					1		1					
2				1		2		1				
3			1		3		3		1			
4		1		4		6		4		1		
5	1		5		10		10		5		1	

and so on

To find the next row of Pascal's triangle you put 1 in both of the outside positions, and then find the number to go in each place by adding the two diagonally above it.

The reason for doing this can be seen by considering the process of obtaining the expansion of $(x + y)^5$ from the known expansion of $(x + y)^4$. This involves multiplying $x^4 + 4x^3 y + 6x^2 y^2 + 4xy^3 + y^4$ by $x + y$ and then collecting like terms.

For example, the term in $x^3 y^2$ is the sum of the two products $y \times 4x^3 y$ and $x \times 6x^2 y^2$, giving the coefficient $4 + 6 = 10$, and the 4 and 6 are the entries in row 4 diagonally above the first entry 10 in row 5.

The numbers in row 5 are

$$1 \quad 5 \quad 10 \quad 10 \quad 5 \quad 1$$

so row 6 is

$$1 \quad 6 \quad 15 \quad 20 \quad 15 \quad 6 \quad 1$$

Pascal's triangle is a quick and easy way of working out the binomial coefficients if n is not too large. However, it soon becomes cumbersome, particularly if you only want to work out a single coefficient.

You will probably have noticed that Pascal's triangle has strong connections with the table values of ^nC_r given on page 135. The values agree up to $n = 6$. Moreover, Pascal's triangle and the table have the same 'law of growth': the addition of values diagonally above for Pascal's triangle and the property $^{n+1}C_{r+1} = {^nC_r} + {^nC_{r+1}}$ for the table (you should convince yourself that these amount to the same thing by looking at some particular cases, e.g. $n = 4$, $r = 1$). Therefore the initial agreement must continue and so Pascal's triangle and the table of values of ^nC_r give the same information (which, of course, is why the ^nC_r are called binomial coefficients).

Values of ^nC_r can also be found from your calculator, or from the Table of binomial coefficients in your student's handbook. Rows which are cut short in this table can be completed by symmetry using $^nC_r = {^nC_{n-r}}$.

EXAMPLE A

Find the first four terms of the expansions of (i) $(x+y)^{17}$ (ii) $(x+y)^{25}$.

SOLUTION

(i) From the $n = 17$ row of the table of binomial coefficients

$$(x+y)^{17} = x^{17} + 17x^{16}y + 136x^{15}y^2 + 680x^{14}y^3 + \cdots$$

(ii) The table stops before $n = 25$, so you use $^nC_r = \dfrac{n!}{r!(n-r)!}$ to find the coefficients:

$$(x+y)^{25} = {}^{25}C_0 x^{25} + {}^{25}C_1 x^{24}y + {}^{25}C_2 x^{23}y^2 + {}^{25}C_3 x^{22}y^3 + \cdots$$
$$= x^{25} + 25x^{24}y + 300x^{23}y^2 + 2300x^{22}y^3 + \cdots$$

EXERCISE A

1 Write out these binomial expansions in full:
   (i) $(a+b)^2$ (ii) $(c+d)^3$ (iii) $(e+f)^4$ (iv) $(l+m)^5$
   (v) $(p+q)^6$ (vi) $(s+t)^8$.

2 Find the terms requested in these binomial expansions:
   (i) The term in n^2y^3 in $(n+y)^5$.
   (ii) The term in q^6p^4 in $(q+p)^{10}$.
   (iii) The first four terms of $(h+k)^{18}$.
   (iv) The first three and last three terms of $(q+pt)^{27}$.

3 (i) Work out the sum of the coefficients in each of the first six rows of the table of binomial coefficients.

   (ii) Make a conjecture about the value of $\displaystyle\sum_{r=0}^{n} {}^nC_r$. Prove your conjecture.

   [Hint: put $x = y = 1$ in a suitable binomial expansion.]

Answers

Chapter 1

? (Page 2)

The editor has explained clearly why the investigation is worth doing: there is growing concern about cycling accidents involving children.

Good quality data is data that best represents the research topic: in this case it is to establish whether or not the number of accidents is significant.

? (Page 3)

The reporter is focusing on two aspects of the investigation: he is looking at cycling accidents in the area over a period of time and he is considering the distribution of ages of accident victims.

Another thing he might consider is to investigate accidents in a similar community in order to be able to make comparisons.

? (Page 6)

Not all the branches have leaves. However, all the branches must be shown in order to show correctly the shape of the distribution.

? (Page 8)

If the basic stem and leaf plot has too many lines, you may *squeeze* it as shown below. In doing this you lose some of the information but you should get a better idea of the shape of the distribution.

Unsqueezed

30 | 2 represents 3.02

```
30 | 2 6
31 | 4
32 | 0 5
33 | 3
34 | 3 6 7
35 | 0 3 4 4 8
36 | 0 0 4 4 4
37 | 0 1 1 3 3 4 8
38 | 3 3 3 5
39 | 0 0 4
40 | 2
41 | 0 0 1 1 4 4
42 |
43 | 0 2 4
```

Squeezed

The data is rounded to one decimal place, so 3.02 becomes 3.0 etc.

3* | 0 represents 3.0

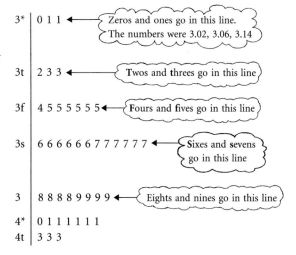

```
3* | 0 1 1        Zeros and ones go in this line.
                  The numbers were 3.02, 3.06, 3.14

3t | 2 3 3        Twos and threes go in this line

3f | 4 5 5 5 5 5 5 Fours and fives go in this line

3s | 6 6 6 6 6 6 7 7 7 7 7 7  Sixes and sevens
                             go in this line

3  | 8 8 8 8 9 9 9 9  Eights and nines go in this line

4* | 0 1 1 1 1 1 1
4t | 3 3 3
```

❷ (Page 9)

Positive and negative data can be represented on a stem and leaf diagram in the following way.

Data set:

−36 −32 −28 −25 −24 −20 −18
        −15 −12   5   8   12   13   18   26

$n = 15$

−3 | 2 represents −32

```
−3 | 6 2
−2 | 8 5 4 0
−1 | 8 5 2
 0 | 5 8
 1 | 2 3 8
 2 | 6
```

Exercise 1A (Page 9)

1 3.27, 3.32, 3.36, 3.43, 3.45, 3.49, 3.50, 3.52, 3.56, 3.56, 3.58, 3.61, 3.61, 3.64, 3.72

2 0.083, 0.086, 0.087, 0.090, 0.091, 0.094, 0.098, 0.102, 0.103, 0.105, 0.108, 0.109, 0.109, 0.110, 0.111, 0.114, 0.123, 0.125, 0.131

3 $n = 13$

21 | 2 represents 0.212

```
21 | 2
22 | 3 6
23 | 0 3 7
24 | 1 2 8
25 | 3 3 9
26 | 2
```

4 $n = 10$

780 | 1 represents 78.01

```
780 | 1
790 | 4 6
800 | 4 8
810 | 3 7 9
820 | 0 5
```

5 0.013, 0.089, 1.79, 3.43, 3.51, 3.57, 3.59, 3.60, 3.64, 3.66, 3.68, 3.71, 3.71, 3.73, 3.78, 3.79, 3.80, 3.85, 3.94, 7.42, 10.87

6 (i) $n = 40$

2 | 8 represents 28 years of age

```
0 | 5
1 | 9
2 | 8 8 2 6 6 9 9
3 | 8 7 4 5 7 8 8 6 3 7 9 5 5 2 6 9 3
4 | 4 6 5 5 1
5 | 2 9 5
6 | 2 0 6 1 3
7 |
8 | 1
```

(ii) Two outliers, 5 years which is obviously a mistake and 81 years which is possible.

7 (i) 16 years of age is a (low) outlier but (with parental permission) it is possible that somebody that age got married. 83 years of age is unusual but not unknown.

(ii) 83 years.

(iii)

```
1 | 6 8 9 9
2 | 0 1 1 1 2 3 4 5 6 6 7 8 8 9
3 | 0 0 0 1 2 2 3 5 9
4 | 3 3 4 5 5 6 6 7 8 9
5 | 1 2 2 7
6 |
7 |
8 | 3
```

(iv)

```
1* |
1  | 6 8 9 9
2* | 0 1 1 1 2 3 4
2  | 5 6 6 7 8 8 9
3* | 0 0 0 1 2 2 3
3  | 5 9
4* | 3 3 4
4  | 5 5 6 6 7 8 9
5* | 1 2 2
5  | 7
6* |
6  |
7* |
7  |
8* | 3
```

(v) The stem and leaf diagram with steps of 10 suggests a slight positive skew.

The stretched stem and leaf diagram shows a clear bimodal spread to the distribution. The first peak (20s) may indicate first marriages and the second peak (40s) may indicate second marriages.

8 $n = 13$

5 | 5 | 7 represents 5.5% (1992) and
5.7% (1991)

```
    6 5 |  1 |
  6 2 9 3 |  2 | 8 8
          |  3 | 9 4 3
    1 0 1 |  4 |
      6 5 |  5 | 7
        1 |  6 | 9 8 5 6 7
        9 |  7 |
          |  8 | 9
          |  9 |
          | 10 | 9
```

Overall there has been a reduction in inflation. However, it is worth noting that the diagram has lost the comparison from 1991 to 1992 for each country. For example the UK more than halved its inflation but in Germany inflation increased significantly.

❷ (Page 17)
The median as it is not affected by the extreme values.

Exercise 1B (Page 17)

1 (i) mode $= 45$, mean $= 39.6$, mid-range $= 37$, median $= 41$
(ii) bimodal, 116 and 132, mean $= 122.5$, mid-range $= 124$, median $= 122$
(iii) mode $= 6$, mean $= 5.3$, mid-range $= 5$, median $= 6$

2 (i) (a) mode $= 14$ years 8 months, mean $= 14$ years 5.5 months, mid-range $= 14$ years 6 months, median $= 14$ years 6 months
(b) Small data set so mode is inappropriate. You would expect all the students in one class to be uniformly spread between 14 years 0 months and 15 years, so any of the other measures would be acceptable, though the mid-range is easiest to calculate.
(ii) (a) mode $= 4$, mean $= 3.85$, mid-range $= 3.75$, median $= 4$
(b) The mean and mid-range do not give very meaningful statistics. The mode is the most representative statistic though in such an example it should be no surprise that the median has the same value.

(iii) (a) bimodal, 0 and 4, mean $= 2.5$, mid-range $= 4$, median $= 3$
(b) The median probably gives the most representative data but the mean allows the researcher to retain the total quantity of beer drunk (mean × sample size) and this may be more useful depending on the aim of the survey.
(iv) (a) mode $= 0$, mean $= 52.8$, mid-range $= 50$, median $= 58$
(b) The median. Small sample makes the mode unreliable and the mean and mid-range are influenced by outliers.
(v) (a) mode $= 0$ and 21 (bimodal), mean $= 29.4$, mid-range $= 84.5$, median $= 20$
(b) Small sample so the mode is inappropriate; the mean and mid-range are affected by outliers, so the median is the best choice.
(vi) (a) no unique mode, mean $= 3.45$, mid-range $= 3.5$, median $= 3.5$.
(b) Anything but the mode will do. The distribution, uniform in theory, means that mean = mid-range = median. This sample reflects that well.

Exercise 1C (Page 20)

1 (i) mode $= 2$
(ii) median $= 3$
(iii) mid-range $= 3.5$
(iv) mean $= 3.24$

2 (i) mode $= 39$
(ii) median $= 40$
(iii) mid-range $= 40.5$
(iv) mean $= 40.3$
(v) The sample has a slight positive skew. Any of the measures would do; however, the mean allows one to calculate the total number of matches.

3 (i) mode $= 19$
(ii) median $= 18$
(iii) mid-range $= 13.5$
(iv) mean $= 17.9$
(v) The outliers affect the mean and mid-range. As the distribution is, apart from the extremes, reasonably symmetrical, the median or mode are acceptable. The median is the safest for a relatively small data set.

4 (i) mode $= 1$, median $= 1$, mid-range $= 5$, mean $= 1.4$
(ii) the median

5 (i) mode $= 1$, mean $= 2.1$, mid-range $= 3.5$,
median $= 2$

(ii) the median

? (Page 23)

The upper boundaries are not stated. 0– could mean 0–9 or it could mean at least 0.

? (Page 25)

The mode can be estimated as in this example for a unimodal histogram.

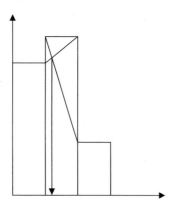

The median can be estimated by interpolation of the interval containing the median or by use of a cumulative frequency curve.

The mid-range can be estimated if you know the least *possible* value in the first interval and the maximum *possible* value in the last interval.

The mean of the original data is 39.73. The estimate is reasonably close at 39.855.

? (Page 26)

The median, as it is least affected by extreme values.

? (Page 27)

The fairest answer is there is not enough information. Ignoring the journalistic prose, '... our town council rate somewhere between savages and barbarians...', the facts given are correct. However, to say whether or not the council is negligent one would need to compare accident statistics with other *similar* communities. Also, one would need to ask who is responsible for a cyclist's risk of having or not having an accident? Perhaps parents should ensure there is adequate training given to their children, and so on.

? (Page 28)

Robert needs to increase his estimate by 0.5 cm (162.32 cm becomes 162.82 cm). The mean of the raw data is 162.86 cm. The estimated value is very close.

Exercise 1D (Page 28)

1 Mid-class values: 114.5, 124.5, 134.5, 144.5, 154.5, 164.5, 174.5, 184.5
Mean $= 161.5$ cm

2 (i) Mid-class values: 24.5, 34.5, 44.5, 54.5, 64.5, 79.5, 104.5
Mean $= 48.5$ minutes

(ii) The second value seems significantly higher. To make the comparison valid the method of data collection would have to be similar, as would the target children sampled.

3 (i) Mid-interval values: 4.5, 14.5, 24.5, 34.5, 44.5, 54.5, 64.5, 74.5, 84.5
Mean (stated age) $= 29.7$

(ii) Add 0.5 mean age $= 30.2$ years

(iii) The estimated mean age once adjusted compares well with the actual mean of 30.4 years.

4 Mean $= 43.1$ cm

5 (i) Class mid-values: 25, 75, 125, 175, 250, 400, 750, 3000
Mean $= 950.1$ m

(ii) The way in which this data is grouped seems to have a marked effect on the mean. This is probably because the distribution is so skewed.

6 (i) $59.5 \leqslant x < 99.5$

(ii) 138.5 g

? (Page 32)

With the item £90 removed the mean $=$ £15.79, compared to £19.50. The extreme value 'dragged' the value of the mean towards it.

? (Page 33)

Each deviation is by definition the data value – the mean. As the mean is *central* to the data, some deviations will be negative (below the mean) and some will be positive (above the mean). The total above the mean cancels out the total below the mean.

? (Page 37)

Using 656 instead of the accurate value of 655.71 ... results in

$$\text{variance} = 430\,041.14 \ldots - 430\,336$$
$$= -294.85 \ldots$$

which, being negative, is impossible.

❷ (Page 38)

With the value 96 omitted the mean $= 54.2$, standard deviation $= 7.9$. The value 96 is more than five standard deviations above the new mean value.

Exercise 1E (Page 39)

1 **(i)** Mean $= 2.36$
(ii) Standard deviation $= 1.49$

2 Mean $= 6.04$, standard deviation $= 1.48$

3 **(i)** Steve: mean $= 1.03$, standard deviation $= 1.05$
Roy: mean $= 1.03$, standard deviation $= 0.55$
(ii) On average they scored the same number of goals but Roy was more consistent.

4 Mean $= 1.1$, standard deviation $= 1.24$

5 Mean $= 0.4$, standard deviation $= 0.4$

6 **(i)** A: mean $= 25\,°C$, standard deviation $= 1.41\,°C$
B: mean $= 25\,°C$, standard deviation $= 2.19\,°C$
(ii) Thermostat A is better. The smaller standard deviation shows it is more consistent in its settings.
(iii) Mean $= 24.8\,°C$, standard deviation $= 1.05\,°C$

7 **(i)** Town route: mean time $= 20$ minutes, standard deviation $= 4.60$ minutes
Country route: mean time $= 20$ minutes, standard deviaiton $= 1.41$ minutes
(ii) Both routes have the same time but the country route is less variable or more consistent.

8 **(i)** Yes. The value is more than two standard deviations above the mean rainfall.
(ii) No. The value is less than one standard deviation below the mean rainfall.
(iii) Overall mean rainfall $= 1.62$ cm, overall standard deviation $= 0.135$ cm
(iv) 84.4 cm

9 **(i)** No. The harvest was less than two standard deviations above the expected value.
(ii) The higher yield was probably the result of the underlying variability but that is likely to be connected to different weather patterns.

10 **(i)** Sample mean $= 2.075$ mm, standard deviation $= 0.185$ mm
(ii) The desired mean is less than 0.5 standard deviations from the observed mean so the machine setting seems acceptable.

11 **(i)** Standard deviation $= 2.54$ cm

(ii) The value 166 cm is less than two standard deviations above 162.82 (Robert's data) and is less than two standard deviations below 170.4 (Asha's data). Consequently it is impossible to say, without further information, which data set it belongs to.

The value 171 is more than three standard deviations above 162.82 and less than one standard deviation above 170.4 so it seems likely that this value is from Asha's data set.

12 Mean $= 6.5$, standard deviation $= 2.08$
Combined data: mean $= 6.76$, standard deviation $= 1.91$

13 **(i)** Total weight $= 3147.72$ g
(ii) $\sum x^2 = 84\,509.9868$
(iii) $n = 200$, $\sum x = 5164.84$, $\sum x^2 = 136\,549.913$
(iv) Mean $= 25.8$ g, standard deviation $= 3.98$ g

14 Monday: $\sum (x - 15)^2 = 120$
Tuesday: $\sum (x - 15)^2 = 125$

$$\text{Standard deviation} = \sqrt{\frac{125 + 120}{50}} = 2.2$$

❷ (Page 44)

Yes but the coded data would have been different: -2, -1, 0, 1, 2, 3.

Exercise 1F (Page 45)

1 Suggested code: $\dfrac{\text{mass} - 254.5}{4}$
Coded data: -3, -2, -1, 0, 1, 2
Mean $= 252.34$ g, standard deviation $= 5.14$ g

2 **(i)** $\bar{x} = -1.7$, $s = 3.43$
(ii) Mean $= 94.83$ mm, standard deviation $= 0.343$ mm
(iii) -18 more than four standard deviations below the mean value.
(iv) New mean $= 94.863$ mm, new standard deviation $= 0.255$ mm

3 **(i)** £73.98, £20.09
(ii) £86.93, £23.61

4 **(i)** Mean $= 6.19$, standard deviation $= 0.484$
(ii) Mean $= 6.68$, standard deviation $= 1.26$

5 **(i)** No unique mode (5 & 6), mean $= 5$, mid-range $= 5$, median $= 5$
(ii) 50 & 60, 50, 50, 50
(iii) 15 & 16, 15, 15, 15
(iv) 10 & 12, 10, 10, 10

6 (i) $\bar{x} = -4.3$ cm, $s = 13.98$ cm

(ii) Mean length $= 99.957$ m, standard deviation length $= 0.140$ m

(iii) -47 is many more than two standard deviations from the mean.

(iv) -2.05, 10.24

Exercise 1G (Page 47)

1

$n = 87$

1 | 8 represents 18 marks

```
 1 | 8 7
 2 | 6 9 2 6 5
 3 | 7 4 4 0 9 2 7 7 0 9 5 6
 4 | 4 5 3 9 0 4 6 4 9 5 0 8
 5 | 4 0 4 1 2 9 1 7 4 2 1 3 6 5
 6 | 6 6 9 8 8 0 1 6 2 6 9 7 5 4
 7 | 6 1 5 4 0 7 6 5 3 4 0
 8 | 0 7 2 7
 9 | 0 5 6 5 7 8 7 2 0 4 1
10 | 0 0
```

The distribution is symmetrical apart from a peak in the 90s. There is a large concentration of marks between 30 and 80.

2 (i)

$n = 40$

1 | 9 represents 19 years of age

```
1 | 9 9 9 7
2 | 8 4 0 8 6 2 5 6 2 6 6 9 3 3 1 8 1 3
3 | 7 4 5 0 1 0
4 | 0 5
5 | 8 8 7
6 | 5 6 9 5 5 7
7 | 2
```

(ii) The distribution is bimodal. This is possibly because those who hang-glide are the reasonably young and active (average age about 25 years) and those who are retired and have taken it up as a hobby (average age about 60).

3

$n = 50$

7|5| means 57 kg (untreated)

Untreated		Treated
8 5 5 8	0	
2 4 0 4 2 7 2 4 6 0 4 1	1	9 8 8
2 9 9 5 0 0 2 2	2	5 6 4 3 5 3 7 4 3 0 1 5
3 2 0 0 1	3	2 3 5 0 3 1 5 8 0 1 3 5 8 8 3
2 3 8 1 0 8 5 0	4	4 7 2 1 1 4 9 4 2
0 6 1 3 8 2 5 1	5	9 2 4 3 3 4 0
1 3 2 1 1	6	1 2 1 3

GRO seems to have improved the yield of lime trees, though there are a significant number of untreated trees that are matching the yield of the treated trees.

4 (i)

$n = 25$

11 | 4 represents 1.14 metres

```
11 | 4 5 8
12 | 1 4 6 6 8 9 9
13 | 0 0 0 0 0 2 2 3 3
14 | 0 1 2 6
15 | 4
16 | 5
```

(ii) 1.46, 1.18

(iii) 1.30

(iv) The median 1.30 is close to the middle value of this range (1.32) so the median seems a reasonable estimate of the length.

5 (i) Mean $= £4200$, median $= £3700$, mode $= £3500$

(ii) Standard deviation $= £2200$

(iii) £11 000 is more than two standard deviations above the mean and can therefore be regarded as an outlier.

(iv) Mean in part (i) is per school and it is unlikely that each school will have the same number of pupils.

6 (i)

$n = 14$

4 | 7 represents 47

```
4 | 7 9
5 | 9
6 | 8 2 7 6 8
7 | 3 0 4 2
8 | 4 0
```

Some negative skew, but otherwise a fairly normal shape.

(ii) Mean $= 67.07$; standard deviation $= 9.97$

(iii) $\bar{c} = \frac{5}{9}(\bar{f} - 32) = \frac{5}{9}(67.07 - 32) = 19.48$

$sd_c = \frac{5}{9}sd_f = \frac{5}{9} \times 9.97 = 5.54$

7 (i) Mean $= 3.382$, standard deviation $= 2.327$

(ii) 4–6 in each case

(iii) Standard deviation for A is greater than the standard deviation for B, since the data for A are more spread out.

(iv) Player A is better; he or she knocks down most of the skittles at the first attempt.

8 (i) A, B and C appear to be compulsory subjects.

(ii) Mean $= 108.75$, median $= 116.5$, mode $= 207$, mid-range $= 106.5$

Mode does not indicate central tendency; others do.

(iii) Standard deviation $= 70.49$

(iv) Total number of subject entries $= 1740$,

$\dfrac{1740}{207} = 8.4$ subjects per pupil

(v) $\dfrac{1740}{79} = 22.0$ pupils per class

9 (i) Mean $= 1.2$, standard deviation $= 3.71$

(ii) 73.2, 3.71

(iii) In the second round the golfers had a better average score and the scores were more consistent.

(iv) Mean $= 72.45$, standard deviation $= 3.41$

10 (i)

$n = 15$

3 | 40 represents £3.40

```
 3 | 40 60 75 95
 4 | 20 50 75
 5 | 20 75
 6 | 45 60
 7 | 25
 8 | 75
 9 | 60
10 |
11 |
12 | 25
```

Median $= £5.20$, range $= £8.85$

(ii) Mean $= £6.00$, standard deviation $= £2.47$

(iii) A: mean $= £6.30$, standard deviation $= £2.47$;
B: mean $= £6.30$, standard deviation $= £2.59$

(iv) Both offers result in the same mean wage and therefore the same *total* wage bill (mean $\times n$). Consequently the financial outlay in each case is the same so either scheme is acceptable to the management. The spread of wages, however, is greater for the 5% rise. Some workers would gain more by accepting this deal (those whose current wage was above the current mean wage). Of course, other workers would gain less by accepting this deal.

11 (i) Mode $= 1$, mid-range $= 4$

(ii) The distribution is unimodal and has positive skew.

(iii) Mean $= 2$, standard deviation $= 1.70$; the value 8 may be regarded as an outlier as it is more than two standard deviations above the mean.

(iv) (a) Exclude it since a difference of 8 is impossible.

(b) Check the validity and include if valid.

(v) Mean $= 1.88$, standard deviation $= 1.48$

Chapter 2

❓ (Page 53)

209 people in Downlee have their own e-mail address (29% of 720). 240 people in Avonford use the Web for at least eight hours per week (50% of 480).

❓ (Page 57)

The ratio of the areas reflects the ratio of the total turnover, that is $3:4$, so the radii are in the ratio $\sqrt{3}:\sqrt{4}$.

The angle subtended at the centre by the sector representing wages is greater in the circle for the year 2000. The actual amount has increased because the total turnover in 2000 is greater.

Bar charts are better as it is easier to read the actual values. Using a pie chart only gives relative values and then only approximately.

Exercise 2A (Page 57)

1 **(i)** **(a)** numerical data/discrete
  (b) a vertical line graph
 (ii) **(a)** categorical
  (b) bar chart
 (iii) **(a)** numerical data/continuous
  (b) histogram or stem and leaf diagram
 (iv) **(a)** categorical data
  (b) bar chart
 (v) **(a)** numerical data/discrete
  (b) vertical line graph
 (vi) **(a)** numerical data/continuous
  (b) histogram or stem and leaf diagram
 (vii) **(a)** categorical data
  (b) bar chart
 (viii) **(a)** numerical data/discrete
  (b) vertical line graph or bar chart
 (ix) **(a)** numerical data/continuous
  (b) histogram or stem and leaf diagram
 (x) **(a)** categorical data
  (b) bar chart

2 Seanna: wool £36 000, kelp £24 000, fish £12 000.
 Rhos Skerry: wool £45 000, kelp £81 000, fish £36 000.

3 (i)

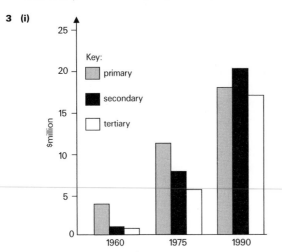

(ii) 1960

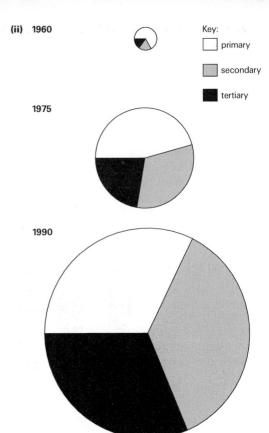

(iii) The education budget has increased over the years and proportionally more has been spent on secondary education until in 1990 it overtakes that spent on primary.

(iv) The bar chart. It shows the relative amounts spent and indicates the actual amounts spent.

4 (i) 1990

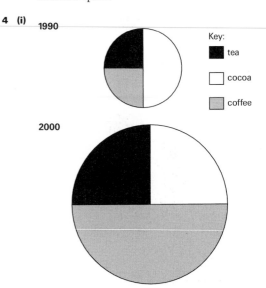

(ii) Crop production has doubled in the period with coffee contributing 50% of all production in 1990 compared to 25% in 1980.

(iii) The bar chart because both the relative and actual values are communicated.

5 (i)

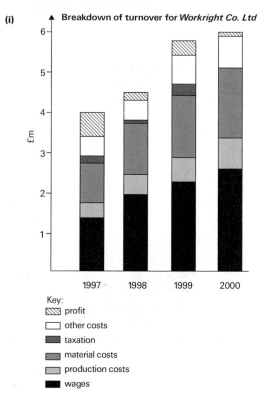

Breakdown of turnover for *Workright Co. Ltd*

Key:
- ▨ profit
- ☐ other costs
- ▨ taxation
- ▨ material costs
- ▨ production costs
- ■ wages

(ii) Sales have increased during the period. However, wages have also increased and profits have decreased.

6

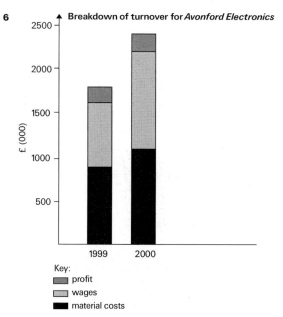

Breakdown of turnover for *Avonford Electronics*

Key:
- ▨ profit
- ▨ wages
- ■ material costs

? **(Page 60)**
You must compare the *frequency density* of each of the intervals.

? **(Page 64)**
The first interval has width 9.5, the last 10.5. All the others are 10. The reason for this is that the data can neither be negative nor exceed 70. So even if part marks were given, and so a mark such as 22.6 was possible, a student still could not obtain less than 0 or more than the maximum of 70.

Exercise 2B (Page 65)

1 (i) $0.5 \leqslant d < 10.5$, $10.5 \leqslant d < 15.5$, $15.5 \leqslant d < 20.5$, $20.5 \leqslant d < 30.5$, $30.5 \leqslant d < 50.5$

(ii)

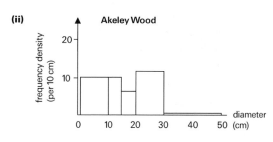

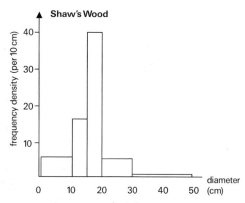

(iii) Akeley Wood: 21–30; Shaw's Wood: 16–20

(iv) For Akeley Wood there is a reasonably even spread of trees with diameters from 0.5 cm to 30.5 cm. For Shaw's Wood the distribution is centred about trees with diameter in the 16–20 cm interval. Neither wood has many trees with diameter greater than 30 cm.

2 (i)

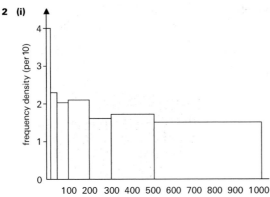

(ii) The distribution has strong positive skew.

3 (i)

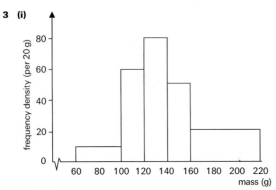

(ii) 138.4 g

4 (i)

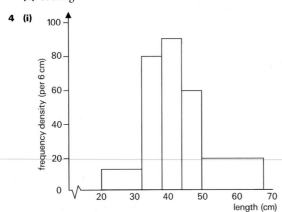

(ii) 42.1 cm

5 (i)

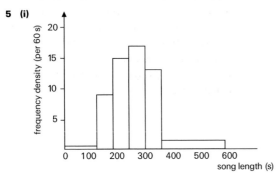

(ii) 264 seconds

? (Page 68)

The data are a sample from a parent population. The true values for the quartiles are those of the parent population, but these are unknown.

Exercise 2C (Page 73)

1 (i) **(a)** 7 **(b)** 6 **(c)** 4.5, 7.5 **(d)** 3

(ii) **(a)** 15 **(b)** 11 **(c)** 8, 14 **(d)** 6

(iii) **(a)** 10 **(b)** 26 **(c)** 23, 28 **(d)** 5

(iv) **(a)** 29 **(b)** 119.5 **(c)** 115.5, 126 **(d)** 10.5

(v) **(a)** 8 **(b)** 5 **(c)** 2.5, 7.5 **(d)** 5

(vi) **(a)** 8 **(b)** 15 **(c)** 12.5, 17.5 **(d)** 5

(vii) **(a)** 8 **(b)** 275 **(c)** 272.5, 227.5 **(d)** 5

(viii) **(a)** 80 **(b)** 50 **(c)** 25, 75 **(d)** 50

2 (i) 74 **(ii)** 73, 76 **(iii)** 3

(iv)

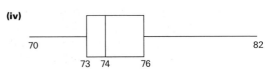

(v) On average the golfers played better in the second round; their average score (median) was four shots better. However, the wider spread of data (the IQR for the second round was twice that for the first) suggests some golfers played very much better but a few played less well.

3 (i)

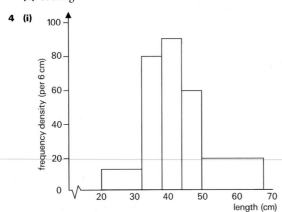

(ii) The vertical line graph as it retains more data for this small sample.

4 (i)

$y \leqslant$	Cumulative frequency
49.5	1
59.5	6
69.5	13
79.5	17
89.5	19
99.5	20

(ii)

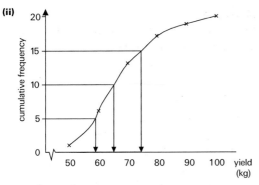

(iii) 65 kg, 16 kg

(iv)

(v) 66 kg, 17.5 kg; the estimated values are quite close to these figures.

(vi) Grouping allows one to get an overview of the distribution but in so doing you lose detail.

Exercise 2D (Page 75)

1 (i)

Status	Interval (pay £P/week)	Frequency (employees)	Interval length (× £10)	Frequency density (employees/ £10)
Unskilled	$120 \leqslant P < 200$	40	8	5.0
Skilled	$200 \leqslant P < 280$	40	8	5.0
Staff	$280 \leqslant P < 400$	30	12	2.5
Management	$400 \leqslant P < 1000$	10	60	0.17

(ii)

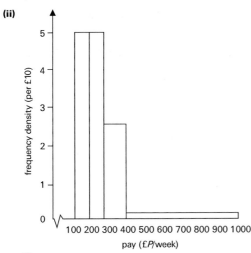

(iii) Yes.

(iv) The two displays emphasise different characteristics of the data. The pie chart draws attention to the relative proportion of workers in each category while the histogram emphasises the concentration of lower-paid workers.

2 (i)

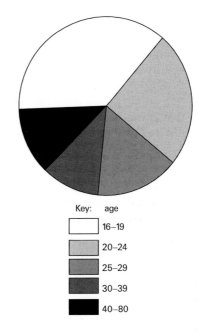

Key: age

- 16–19
- 20–24
- 25–29
- 30–39
- 40–80

(ii) Just turned 16 years of age and *almost* 20 years of age.

(iii)

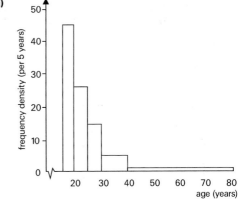

(iv) The distribution has definite positive skew. The age range 16–19 is the most dangerous age range. The range 40–80 is the least dangerous. It is not possible to state which *single* age is the most/least dangerous, though it would be reasonable to estimate that the most dangerous, for example, was somewhere in the range 16–19.

(v) The histogram takes into account the different class widths allowing the reader to see the *concentration* of ages.

3 (i) The data are discrete. 'Numbers of pages' can only take integer values.

(ii) The data are positively skewed. Even though the data are discrete (suggesting a stem and leaf diagram or vertical line graph) the data are very spread out with most of the data values less than 200. A histogram will show the distribution properties best.

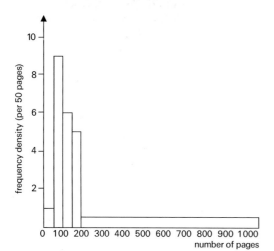

4 (i)

(ii) 11.0 s, 11.0 s

(iii) 13.5 s

5

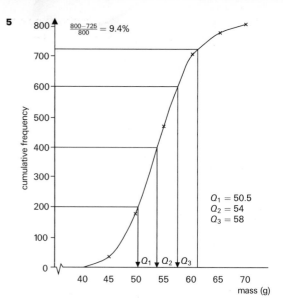

$\frac{800-725}{800} = 9.4\%$

$Q_1 = 50.5$
$Q_2 = 54$
$Q_3 = 58$

(i) 9.4%   **(ii)** 54 g   **(iii)** 7.5 g

6 (i) 64.1 years

(ii) 66.5, 74.7, 55.7.

(iii)

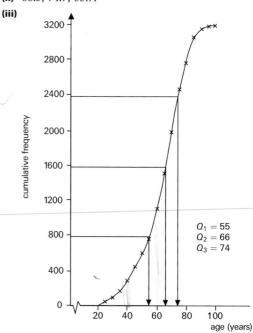

$Q_1 = 55$
$Q_2 = 66$
$Q_3 = 74$

66, 74, 55. Values very close to calculated values.

7 (i)

Length of leaf (mm)	Cumulative frequency Strain A	Strain B
⩽9.5	3	1
⩽14.5	9	5
⩽19.5	20	11
⩽24.5	42	21
⩽29.5	77	37
⩽34.5	88	62
⩽39.5	94	82
⩽44.5	98	93
⩽49.5	99	97
>49.5	100	100

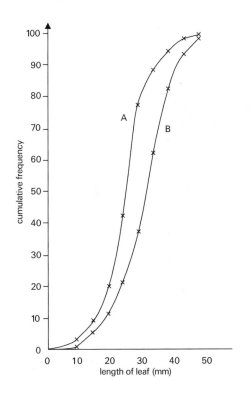

(ii) (a) Strain B is better for longer leaves; median = 32.5 mm, compared with 25.1 mm for B.

(b) Nothing much to choose between the strains for uniformity; the IQR for each is similar, for A: 8, for B: 9, so the level of variability is similar.

8 (i) Men in both categories (manual and non-manual) earn on average over £100 per week more than women.

(ii) Manual (men): $IQR=$£106
Manual (women): $IQR=$£59
Earnings by men more variable, roughly twice as much.
Non-manual (men): $IQR=$£183
Non-manual (women): $IQR=$£117
Earnings by men, again, more variable.

9 (i) 12.2 s, 6.11 s

(ii)

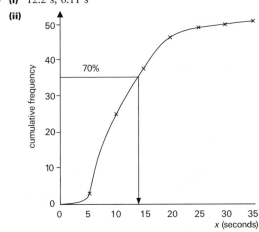

14.5 seconds

10 6.0 volts, 0.067 volts

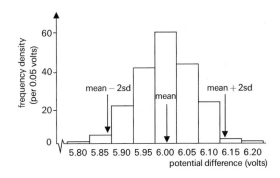

Chapter 3

Exercise 3A (Page 89)

1 $\frac{66}{534}$, assuming each faulty torch has only one fault.

2 (i) $\frac{1}{6}$ **(ii)** $\frac{3}{6}$ **(iii)** $\frac{3}{6}$ **(iv)** $\frac{3}{6}$

3 (i) $\frac{12}{98}$ **(ii)** $\frac{53}{98}$ **(iii)** $\frac{45}{98}$ **(iv)** $\frac{42}{98}$ **(v)** $\frac{56}{98}$ **(vi)** $\frac{5}{98}$

4 (i) $\frac{5}{2000}$ **(ii)** $\frac{1995}{2000}$ **(iii)** Lose £100, if all tickets are sold. **(iv)** 25p **(v)** 2500

5 (i) 0.35 **(ii)** They might draw. **(iii)** 0.45 **(iv)** 0.45

6 (i)

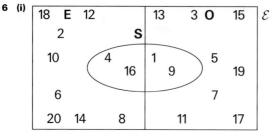

(ii) (a) $\frac{10}{20}$ **(b)** $\frac{4}{20}$ **(c)** $\frac{10}{20}$ **(d)** $\frac{2}{20}$ **(e)** $\frac{12}{20}$ **(f)** 0 **(g)** 1
(h) $P(E \cup S) = P(E) + P(S) - P(E \cap S)$
(i) $P(E \cup O) = P(E) + P(O) - P(E \cap O)$

7 (i) 0.22 **(ii)** 0.40 **(iii)** 0.10 **(iv)** 0.65 **(v)** 0.35

Exercise 3B (Page 97)

1

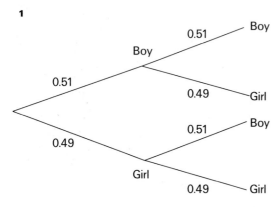

(i) 0.2401 **(ii)** 0.5002 **(iii)** 0.4998

2

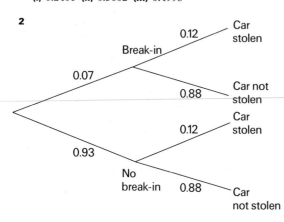

(i) 0.0084 **(ii)** 0.1732 **(iii)** 0.1816

3 $\frac{1}{12}$

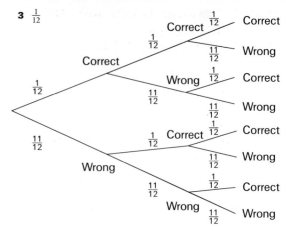

(i) (a) 0.00058 **(b)** 0.77 **(c)** 0.020
(ii) (a) 0.0052 **(b)** 0.52 **(c)** 0.094

4 0.93

5

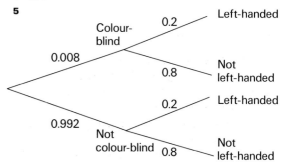

(i) 0.0016 **(ii)** 0.0064 **(iii)** 0.2064 **(iv)** 0.7936

6 $\frac{3}{4}$

7 (i) 0.2436 **(ii)** 0.7564 **(iii)** 0.2308 **(iv)** 0.4308

8 (i) 0.0741 **(ii)** 0.5787 **(iii)** 0.5556

9 For a sequence of events you multiply the probabilities. However, $\frac{1}{6} \times \frac{1}{6} \times \frac{1}{6} \times \frac{1}{6} \times \frac{1}{6} \times \frac{1}{6}$ gives the probability of six 6s in six throws. To find the probability of at least one 6 you need $1 - P$ (No 6s) and that is $1 - \frac{5}{6} \times \frac{5}{6} \times \frac{5}{6} \times \frac{5}{6} \times \frac{5}{6} \times \frac{5}{6} = 0.665$.

10 0.5833

11

Green die

+	1	2	3	4	5	6
1	2	3	4	5	6	7
2	3	4	5	6	7	8
Red **3**	4	5	6	7	8	9
die **4**	5	6	7	8	9	10
5	6	7	8	9	10	11
6	7	8	9	10	11	12

(ii) $\frac{3}{36}$ **(iii)** 7 **(iv)** The different outcomes are not all equally probable.

12 (i) $\frac{1}{2}$ **(ii)** $\frac{1}{8}$ **(iii)** $\frac{3}{8}$ **(iv)** 62.5p

13 0.31

14 (i) 0.1667 **(ii)** 0.1389 **(iii)** 0.1157 **(iv)** 0.5787

15 (i) $\frac{11}{12}$ **(iii)** 0.382 **(iv)** 0.618

16 (i) $\frac{1}{4}$ **(ii)** $\frac{81}{256}$ **(iii)** $\frac{81}{1024}$ **(iv)** $\frac{1}{16}$ **(v)** $\frac{3}{4}$ **(vi)** $\frac{3}{32}$

? (Page 104)

$P(T \mid S) = \frac{109}{169} = 0.645$

$P(T \mid S') = \frac{43}{87} = 0.494$

So $P(T \mid S) \neq P(T \mid S')$

T those who had training; T' those with no training; S those who stayed in the company; $\mathcal{E}$ all employees.

S' is inside the $\mathcal{E}$ box but not in the S region.

For example, in part (i), the answer is $\frac{152}{256}$. 152 is in T (but not in T'), 256 is everyone.

? (Page 106)

The first result was used in answering part (i) and the second result in answering part (iii).

Exercise 3C (Page 107)

1 (i) 0.6 **(ii)** 0.556 **(iii)** 0.625 **(iv)** 0.047 **(v)** 0.321
  (vi) 0.075 **(vii)** 0.028 **(viii)** 0.0022 **(ix)** 0.000 95 **(x)** 0.48

2 (i) (a) 0.160 **(b)** 0.120 **(c)** 0.400 **(d)** 0.160
  (e) 0.003 **(f)** 0.088 **(g)** 0.018

  (ii) Those sentenced for motoring offences would probably have shorter sentences than others so are likely to represent less than 2% of the prison population at any time.

3 (i) $\frac{35}{100}$ **(ii)** $\frac{42}{100}$ **(iii)** $\frac{15}{65}$

4 (i) $\frac{1}{6}$ **(ii)** $\frac{5}{12}$ **(iii)** $\frac{2}{5}$

5 (i) $\frac{7}{15}$ **(ii)** $\frac{11}{21}$ **(iii)** $\frac{5}{21}$ **(iv)** $\frac{5}{11}$

6 (i) 30 **(ii)** $\frac{7}{40}$ **(iii)** $\frac{7}{10}$ **(iv)** $\frac{7}{15}$

7 (i) $\frac{7}{10}$ **(ii)** $\frac{19}{40}$ **(iii)** $\frac{10}{19}$

8 (i) 0.497 **(ii)** 0.477 **(iii)** 0.222 **(iv)** 0.461

9 (i) 0.5 and 0.875

  (ii) $P(B \mid A) \neq P(B)$ and $P(A \mid B) \neq P(A)$ so the events A and B are not independent.

10 (i)

	Hunter dies	Hunter lives	
Quark dies	$\frac{1}{12}$	$\frac{5}{12}$	$\frac{1}{2}$
Quark lives	$\frac{2}{12}$	$\frac{1}{3}$	$\frac{1}{2}$
	$\frac{1}{4}$	$\frac{3}{4}$	1

  (ii) $\frac{1}{12}$ **(iii)** $\frac{5}{12}$ **(iv)** $\frac{5}{6}$

11 (i)

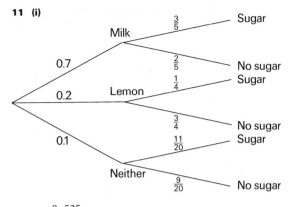

0 .525

(ii) 0.805 **(iii)** 0.42; 0.8

12 (i)

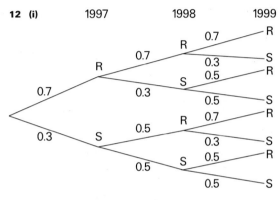

(ii) 0.372 **(iii)** 0.395 **(iv)** 8

13 (i)

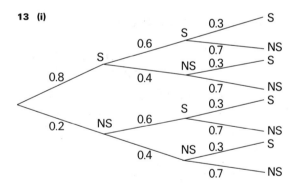

(ii) 0.056 **(iii)** 0.332 **(iv)** 0.675 **(v)** $\frac{14}{41}$

14 (i)

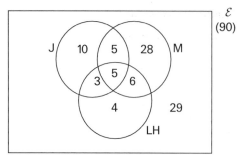

Key:
J = Juniors
M = Males
LH = Left-handed players

(ii) (a) $\frac{1}{4}$ (b) $\frac{1}{6}$ (c) $\frac{28}{45}$ (d) $\frac{4}{5}$ (e) $\frac{19}{24}$ (f) $\frac{10}{39}$

Chapter 4

❷ (Page 115)

1 The population is made up of the M.P.'s constituents.

The sample is a part of that population of constituents. Without information relating to how the constituents' views were elicited, the views obtained seem to be biased towards those constituents who bother to write to their M.P.

2 The population is made up of Manchester households.

We are not told how the sample is chosen. Even if a random sample of households were chosen the views obtained are still likely to be biased as the interview timing excludes the possibility of obtaining views of most of those residents in employment.

3 The population is made up of black residents in Chicago.

The sample is made up of black people (and possibly some white people as the areas are 'predominantly black') from a number of areas in Chicago.

The survey may be biased in two ways:

(i) the areas may not be representative of all residential areas and therefore of all black people living in Chicago and

(ii) given that negative police officers are carrying out the survey they are unlikely to obtain negative views.

❷ (Page 116)

1 Each student is equally likely to be chosen but samples including two or more students from the same class are not permissible so not all samples are equally likely.

2 Yes

Exercise 4A (Page 118)

1 (i) Systematic sampling
  (ii) (a) Simple random sampling
    (b) $\frac{1}{25}$
  (iii) (a) Cluster sampling
    (b) No. The streets are chosen at random and then 15 houses are chosen at random. However, not every sample of size 15 (throughout the town) can be chosen.
  (iv) (a) Quota sampling
    (b) No
    (c) The sample is small. It is questionable how reliable such information would be.

2 (i) (a) Years 1 and 2: 7 students from each; Years 3 and 4: 5 students from each; Year 5: 6 students.
    (b) $\frac{1}{20}$
  (ii) (a) 28 light vans, 2 company cars and 1 large-load vehicle.
    (b) Randomly choose the appropriate number of vehicles from each type. This is stratified sampling.
  (iii) (a) $\frac{1}{8}$
    (b) 0–5: 5; 6–12: 10; 13–21: 13 or 14; 22–35: 25 or 26; 36–50: 22 or 23; 51+: 3 or 4.

3 (i) Cluster sampling. Choose representative streets or areas and sample from these streets or areas.
  (ii) Stratified sample. Identify routes of interest and randomly sample trains from each route.
  (iii) Stratified sample. Choose representative areas in the town and randomly sample from each area as appropriate.
  (iv) Stratified sample as in part (iii).
  (v) Depends on method of data collection. If survey is, say, via a postal enquiry, then a random sample may be selected from a register of addresses.
  (vi) Cluster sample. Routes and times are chosen and a traffic sampling station is established to randomly stop vehicles to test tyres.
  (vii) Cluster sampling. Areas are chosen and households are then randomly chosen.
  (viii) Cluster sampling. A period (or periods) is chosen to sample and speeds are surveyed.
  (ix) Cluster sampling. Meeting places for 18-year-olds are identified: night clubs, pubs etc. and samples of 18-year-olds are surveyed, probably via a method to maintain privacy. This might be a questionnaire to ascertain required information.
  (x) Random sample. The school pupil list is used as a sampling frame to establish a random sample within the school.

4 (i) Systematic sampling. Easy to set up but may be difficult to track down the student once they have been identified.

(ii) Stratified sampling. Will reflect all opinions, but only as defined by the surveyor. Easy to carry out. That is, it should be easy to access the desired sample, students as they enter the college premises.

(iii) The sample will be biased. Easy to survey. Those using the canteen will be surveyed.

(iv) Cluster sampling. Assumes first and second year students are representative of the whole college. (If there are only first and second year students this will be true. The sampling procedure is then stratified.) Similar to (i), that is, once students have been chosen from the lists they have to be located to seek their views.

5 (i) All production lines are identified. If it is judged they are equivalent then one (or more) can be chosen to produce a sample. This is cluster sampling. From this (or these) production line(s) a day (or days) is chosen to be the time when a sample is taken. A reasonable number of strip lights is chosen and then tested to destruction, that is, tested until they are exhausted. An estimate is found from the mean life of the sample chosen.

(ii) The map of the forest is covered with a grid. Each grid square is numbered. A sample is chosen by randomly selecting the squares. The tree (or trees) in each of the chosen squares is sampled.

(iii) (a) A sample of 100 chips to be taken from each production line each working day (assuming a five day week).

(b) Stratified.

(iv) Depending on the number of staff, one could carry out a census of all staff or, if more appropriate, a stratified sample based on part-time staff, full-time staff, etc.

(v) Identify different courses in your school/college. Access pupils from each of the courses, choosing them at random in order to elicit their views. This is a stratified sample.

Chapter 5

❷ (Page 129)
Gary could have put the bricks in order by chance. A probability of $\frac{1}{120}$ is small but not very small. What would really be convincing is if he could repeat the task whenever he was given the bricks.

Exercise 5A (Page 131)

1 (i) 40 320 **(ii)** 56 **(iii)** $\frac{5}{7}$

2 (i) $\frac{1}{n}$ **(ii)** $n-1$

3 (i) $(n+3)(n+2)$ **(ii)** $n(n-1)$

4 (i) $\dfrac{8! \times 2!}{5! \times 5!}$ **(ii)** $\dfrac{16!}{14! \times 4!}$ **(iii)** $\dfrac{(n+1)!}{(n-2)! \times 4!}$

5 (i) $9 \times 7!$ **(ii)** $n!(n+2)$

6 24

7 40 320

8 720

9 (i) 120 **(ii)** $\frac{1}{120}$

10 14! **(ii)** $\dfrac{1}{14!}$

11 (i) $\dfrac{1}{10!}$ **(ii)** Lose 7.2p **(iii)** £362 000 (to the nearest £1000)

12 $\frac{6}{24} = \frac{1}{4}$ (OPTS, POST, POTS, SPOT, STOP, TOPS)

❷ (Page 133)
No it does not matter.

❷ (Page 133)
Multiply top and bottom by 43!

$$\frac{49 \times 48 \times 47 \times 46 \times 45 \times 44}{6!} \times \frac{43!}{43!} = \frac{49!}{6! \, 43!}$$

❷ (Page 134)
$$^{49}C_6 = 13\,983\,816 \approx 14 \text{ million}$$

❷ (Page 134)
By following the same argument as for the National Lottery example but with n for 49 and r for 6.

❷ (Page 134)
$$^{n}C_0 = \frac{n!}{0! \, n!} = 1 \qquad \text{if } 0! = 1$$
$$^{n}C_n = \frac{n!}{n! \, (n-n)!} = 1 \qquad \text{again if } 0! = 1$$

❷ (Page 136)
$$\text{R.H.S} = \frac{n!}{r!(n-r)!} + \frac{n!}{(r+1)!(n-r-1)!}$$
$$= \frac{n!}{r!(n-r-1)!}\left[\frac{1}{n-r} + \frac{1}{r+1}\right]$$
$$= \frac{n!}{r!(n-r-1)!}\left[\frac{r+1+n-r}{(n-r)(r+1)}\right]$$
$$= \frac{(n+1)!}{(r+1)!(n-r)!}$$
$$= {}^{n+1}C_{r+1} = \text{L.H.S.}$$

❓ (Page 138)

1 The probability is $\frac{1}{24}$, assuming the selection is done at random, so Agnes is not justified when she says 'less than one in a hundred'.

2 As a product of probabilities $\frac{1}{3} \times \frac{1}{2} \times \frac{1}{4} = \frac{1}{24}$

Exercise 5B (Page 138)

1 **(i)** **(a)** 30 **(b)** 1680 **(c)** 5040
  (ii) **(a)** 15 **(b)** 70 **(c)** 210
2 $\frac{1}{2730}$
3 $\frac{1}{593\,775}$
4 715
5 280
6 **(i)** 31 824 **(ii)** 3000
7 **(i)** 210 **(ii)** **(a)** $\frac{1}{14}$ **(b)** $\frac{3}{7}$
8 **(i)** 715 **(ii)** 5 **(iii)** $\frac{1}{143}$
  (iv) The applicants are all equally suitable and so the jobs are given at random.
9 **(i)** 126 **(ii)** **(a)** $\frac{1}{126}$ **(b)** $\frac{45}{126}$
10 **(i)** $\frac{1}{120}$ **(ii)** $\frac{1}{7\,893\,600}$
11 **(i)** 495 **(ii)** 45 **(iii)** $\frac{1}{11}$ **(iv)** 210 **(v)** $\frac{24}{210}$
12 **(i)** 65 780 **(ii)** $\frac{1}{65\,780}$
  (iii) There are 5 ways of getting 4 letters out of 5. There are 21 other possible letters for 5th letter: $5 \times 21 = 105$
  (iv) 2100 **(v)** $\dfrac{(2100 + 105 + 1)}{65\,780} = \dfrac{1}{29.8}$

Chapter 6

Exercise 6A (Page 146)

1 $\frac{15}{64}$
2 0.271
3 0.214
4 0.294
5 **(i)** 0.146
  (ii) Poor visibility might depend on the time of day, or might vary with the time of year. If so, this simple binomial model would not be applicable.
6 **(i)** $\frac{1}{8}$ **(ii)** $\frac{3}{8}$ **(iii)** $\frac{3}{8}$ **(iv)** $\frac{1}{8}$
7 **(i)** 0.246 **(ii)** Exactly 7
8 **(i)** **(a)** 0.058 **(b)** 0.198 **(c)** 0.296 **(d)** 0.448 **(ii)** 2
9 **(i)** **(a)** 0.264 **(b)** 0.368 **(c)** 0.239 **(d)** 0.129
  (ii) Assumed the probability of being born in January $= \frac{31}{365}$. This ignores the possibility of leap years and seasonal variations in the pattern of births throughout the year.
10 The three possible outcomes are not equally likely: 'one head and one tail' can arise in two ways (HT or TH) and is therefore twice as probable as 'two heads' (or 'two tails').

Activity (Page 148)

Expectation of $X = \displaystyle\sum_{r=0}^{n} r \times P(X = r)$

Since the term with $r = 0$ is zero

Expectation of $X = \displaystyle\sum_{r=1}^{n} r \times P(X = r)$

$$= \sum_{r=1}^{n} r \times {}^{n}C_r p^r q^{n-r}.$$

The typical term of this sum is

$$r \times \frac{n!}{r!(n-r)!} p^r q^{n-r} = np \times \frac{(n-1)!}{(r-1)!(n-r)!} p^{r-1} q^{n-r}$$

$$= np \times \frac{(n-1)!}{(r-1)!((n-1)-(r-1))!}$$

$$\times p^{r-1} q^{(n-1)-(r-1)}$$

Using $(n-1) - (r-1) = n - r$

$$= np \times {}^{n-1}C_{r-1} p^{r-1} q^{(n-1)-(r-1)}$$

$$= np \times {}^{n-1}C_s p^s q^{(n-1)-s}$$

where $s = r - 1$.

In the summation, np is a common factor and s runs from 0 to $n - 1$ as r runs from 1 to n. Therefore

Expectation of $X = np \times \displaystyle\sum_{s=0}^{n-1} {}^{n-1}C_s p^s q^{(n-1)-s}$

$$= np(q + p)^{n-1}$$

$$= np \qquad \text{since } q + p = 1.$$

Exercise 6B (Page 151)

1 **(i)** **(a)** 0.000 129 **(b)** 0.0322 **(c)** 0.402
  (ii) 0 & 1 equally likely
2 **(i)** 2 **(ii)** 0.388 **(iii)** 0.323
3 **(i)** 0.240 **(ii)** 0.412 **(iii)** 0.265 **(iv)** 0.512 **(v)** 0.384
  (vi) 0.096 **(vii)** 0.317
  Assumption: the men and women in the office are randomly chosen from the population (as far as their weights are concerned).
4 **(i)** **(a)** $\frac{1}{81}$ **(b)** $\frac{8}{81}$ **(c)** $\frac{24}{81}$ **(d)** $\frac{32}{81}$ **(ii)** 2 min 40 s
5 **(i)** He must be an even number of steps from the bar. (The numbers of steps he goes east or west are either both even or both odd, since their sum is 12, and in both cases the difference between them, which gives his distance from the bar, is even.)
  (ii) 0.002 93 **(iii)** At the bar **(iv)** 0.242 **(v)** 2.71
6 **(i)** 0.0735 **(ii)** 2.7 **(iii)** 0.267
7 **(i)** $\frac{32}{243}$ **(ii)** $\frac{192}{243}$ **(iii)** $\frac{40}{243}$ **(iv)** $\frac{242}{243}$

8 **(i)** 0.002 69 **(ii)** 0.121 **(iii)** 0.167 **(iv)** 0.723

9 **(i)** **(a)** 0.195 **(b)** 0.299

  (ii) 3 correct answers most likely; 0.260

10 **(i)** 0.003 22 **(ii)** 0.0193 **(iii)** 0.0386

11 **(iii)** $0.8167^{12} \approx 0.088$ **(iv)** £121.50; 4.05% **(v)** £64.20

12 **(i)** $\frac{1}{64}$ **(ii)** $\frac{15}{64}$ **(iii)** $\frac{45}{512}$ **(iv)** $\frac{45}{2048}$ **(v)** $\frac{405}{8192}$

13 **(i)** 0.99; 0.93

  (ii) 0.356; expected number of boxes with no broken eggs $= 100 \times 0.356 = 35.6$, which agrees well with the observed number, 35.

  (iii) 0.0237

14 **(i)** **(a)** 0.349 **(b)** 0.387 **(c)** 0.194 **(ii)** 0.070 **(iii)** 0.678

Chapter 7

? (Page 158)

Assuming both types of parents have the same fertility, boys born would outnumber girls in the ratio 3 : 1. In a generation's time there would be a marked shortage of women of child-bearing age.

? (Page 163)

$0.9629 - 0.8982$ is $P(X \leqslant 6) - P(X \leqslant 5)$ and so is $P(X = 6)$. You will find the number 0.0647 features in the table on page 161 for 6 successes. This is an easy way of working out such binomial probabilities.

Exercise 7A (Page 163)

1 0.1275 Accept H_0

2 **(i)** 0.180 **(ii)** 0.416

  H_0: probability of passing first test $= 0.6$
  H_1: probability of passing first test < 0.6
  $0 \leqslant N \leqslant 7$

3 0.055 Reject H_0

4 H_0: probability that toast lands butter-side down $= 0.5$
  H_1: probability that toast lands butter-side down > 0.5
  0.240 Accept H_0

5 0.048 Reject H_0

  There is evidence that the complaints are justified at the 5% significance level, though Mr McTaggart might object that the candidates were not randomly chosen.

6 0.104 Accept H_0

  Insufficient evidence at the 5% significance level that the machine needs servicing.

7 **(i)** 2; 1.183

  (ii) P(2 defectives in 10) $= 0.302$

    In 50 samples of 10, the expected number of samples with two defectives is 15.1, which agrees well with the observed 15.

  (iii) H_0: P(mug defective) $= 0.2$
    H_1: P(mug defective) < 0.2
    $n = 20$. P(0 or 1 defective mug) $= 0.011$
    Reject H_0
    It is reasonable to suppose that the proportion of defective mugs has been reduced.

  (iv) Same conclusion

8 **(i)** 0.590 **(ii)** 0.044 **(iii)** 0.000 071 2 **(iv)** 0.0286

  (v) H_0: P(long question right) $= 0.5$
    H_1: P(long question right) > 0.5

  (vi) No

? (Page 168)

Critical region at 10% significance level is $X \leqslant 4$.

Exercise 7B (Page 168)

1 **(i)** Let $p =$ P(business operates no smoking policy)
    H_0: $p = 0.7$, H_1: $p < 0.7$

  (ii) $k \leqslant 10$ **(iii)** $k \leqslant 1$

  (iv) For 19 businesses, P(H_0 rejected) $= 0.1855$
    For 4 businesses, P(H_0 rejected) $= 0.1265$
    The 19 business test is preferable because it gives a greater probability of rejecting H_0 when it should be rejected.

2 **(i)** 0.430 **(ii)** 0.9619 **(iii)** 0.0046

  (iv) H_0: $p = 0.9$, H_1: $p < 0.9$

  (v) $n = 17$; P($X \leqslant 13$) $= 0.0826 > 5\%$;
    not sufficient evidence to reject H_0.

  (vi) Critical region is $X \leqslant 12$, since
    P($X \leqslant 12$) $= 0.0221$.

3 **(i)** **(a)** 0.0278 **(b)** 0.0384

  (ii) Let $p =$ P(blackbird is male)
    H_0: $p = 0.5$, H_1: $p > 0.5$

  (iii) Result is significant at the 5% significance level.
    Critical region is $X \geqslant 12$.

  (iv) You would be more reluctant to accept H_1.
    Although H_0 is still $p = 0.5$, the sampling method is likely to give a non-random sample.

4 **(i)** **(a)** 0.0991 **(b)** 0.1391

  (ii) Let $p =$ P(seed germinates)
    H_0: $p = 0.8$, H_1: $p > 0.8$, since a higher germination rate is suspected.

  (iii) Critical region is $X \geqslant 17$, since
    P($X \geqslant 17$) $= 0.0991 < 10\%$ but
    P($X \geqslant 16$) $= 0.2713 > 10\%$.

  (iv) **(a)** When $p = 0.8$ he reaches the wrong conclusion if he rejects H_0, i.e. if $X \geqslant 17$, with probability 0.0991.

    (b) When $p = 0.82$ he reaches the wrong conclusion if he fails to reject H_0, i.e. if $X \leqslant 16$, with probability
      $1 - 0.1391 = 0.8609$.

Exercise 7C (Page 173)

1 2×0.252 Accept H_0
2 2×0.0106 Reject H_0
3 2×0.073 Accept H_0
4 0.014   Reject H_0 but data not independent.
5 0.102   Accept H_0
6 0.158   Accept H_0
7 $\leqslant 1$ or >9 males
8 $\leqslant 1$ or >8 correct
9 Critical region is $\leqslant 3$ or $\geqslant 13$ letter Zs
10 (i) 20 (ii) 0.0623 (iii) Complaint justified
11 (i) 0.0417 (ii) 0.0592 (iii) 0.0833 (iv) 0.1184
   (v) Let $p = P(\text{man selected})$
       $H_0: p = 0.5$, $H_1: p \neq 0.5$
       $P(X \leqslant 4 \text{ or } X \geqslant 11) = 0.084 > 5\%$
       There is not sufficient evidence to reject H_0, so it
       is reasonable to suppose that the process is
       satisfactory.
   (vi) $4 \leqslant w \leqslant 11$

Appendices

Exercise A (Page 178)

1 (i) $a^2 + 2ab + b^2$ (ii) $c^3 + 3c^2d + 3cd^2 + d^3$
   (iii) $e^4 + 4e^3f + 6e^2f^2 + 4ef^3 + f^4$
   (iv) $l^5 + 5l^4m + 10l^3m^2 + 10l^2m^3 + 5lm^4 + m^5$
   (v) $p^6 + 6p^5q + 15p^4q^2 + 20p^3q^3 + 15p^2q^4 + 6pq^5 + q^6$
   (vi) $s^8 + 8s^7t + 28s^6t^2 + 56s^5t^3 + 70s^4t^4 + 56s^3t^5 + 28s^2t^6 + 8st^7 + t^8$

2 (i) $10n^2y^3$ (ii) $210q^6p^4$
   (iii) $h^{18} + 18h^{17}k + 153h^{16}k^2 + 3060h^{15}k^3$
   (iv) $q^{27} + 27q^{26}pt + 351q^{25}p^2t^2 + \cdots + 351q^2p^{25}t^{25} + 27qp^{26}t^{26} + p^{27}t^{27}$

3 (i) 2, 4, 8, 16, 32, 64
   (ii) $\displaystyle\sum_{r=0}^{n} {}^nC_r = 2^n$

Index